£4:25

DOG TALES:
an anthology collected by
Jean and Frank Jackson.

Printed in Great Britain by
Gibbons Barford, Wolverhampton
and published by
Richard Marples and Partners
5, James Leigh Street
Manchester, M60 1SX

I.S.B.N. 0 903034 09 3

CONTENTS :

Every Pack of any standing maintains
a few Hounds:
Frederick Watson
196

FOREWORD.

The public demand for books about dogs seems to be almost insatiable and yet much of the most valuable and interesting material which has been written in the past now lies buried in books which are no longer widely read or even widely available. This old literature in some cases underlines the changes which have taken place to our attitude towards dogs and the uses we make of them. Equally it also underlines how unchanging is the relationship between man and dog.

This anthology was collected by Jean and Frank Jackson. It reflects both their wide reading and their interests in dogs and I am confident that its contents will find a wide appreciation.

Richard Marples.   1981.

INTRODUCTION.

For a number of years we have been in the habit of jotting down anything we came across which seemed to us to have something worthwhile to say about dogs. Somewhat to our surprise these years of totally indiscriminate reading produced a large though heterogenous collection of prose and poetry, ancient and modern which is united only in that it all in some way or other is about dogs and has attracted and retained our interest. We found that guests enjoyed browsing through our collection and that we too continued to enjoy dipping into it, it thus seemed possible that others too may share our enjoyment

The original random order in which individual pieces appear in our notebooks is here replaced by a roughly chronological order and each piece has been given a title, otherwise they appear here much in the form in which they have been jotted down over the years.

The pieces come from a great many sources, some are well known, some may come as a surprise. Doubtless they reflect both our taste in reading matter and our particular interests in dogs. They demonstrate a respect for all dogs though perhaps a particular respect and admiration for those which are called upon to use their intelligence, to demonstrate their strength, speed and courage or which show unusual sagacity. Those who do appreciate such things we hope will enjoy this book. That is its purpose. It seeks neither to persuade nor to educate. It has no high moral purpose or low political one. It is intended simply to provide enjoyment. For that we make no apology. Enjoyment is what our dogs have given us, as well as so very much more.

If this book is to have a dedication it must be to the dogs which have shared our hearth and our lives and which have given us so much fun. To Laddie and Toby of long ago, to Meg, Gem, Merry, Cetch, Poppy and Nell and to many more. We must also recognise all the other dogs, not our own, which we have admired in the field, at work or at shows, they too have provided us with fun and have won both our respect and our admiration.

Our randomly collected notebooks were given some semblance of order and some pretensions to book form during a few hilarious days with the help and enthusiasm of Dave Barker, Vince Hogan and Bill Moores to whom our thanks.

Jean and Frank Jackson,
Sussex.
1981

ODYSSEUS' HOUND: awaiting his master's
return.

Such things they twain in mutual converse said,
    While in the Court they lingered at the door.
And the dog Argus raised his ears and head,
    Whom the much toiled Odysseus long before
    Reared with his own hand, but enjoyed no more.
Ere the time came, he passed to sacred Troy.
    There lay the dog – whom in the days of yore
Oft did the young men in the chase employ,
Hares and the flying deer and wild goats to destroy

Cast out nor cared for by his master's hand,
    On dung of mules and kine, which there did stay
Heaped till the servants should manure the land,
    Swarming with vermin the dog Argus lay;
    Who, when he marked Odysseus in the way,
And could no longer to his lord come near,
    Fawned with his tail, and drooped in feeble play
His ears. Odysseus turning wiped a tear,

Hid from the noble swineherd, and made question
        there:

'Surely, Eumaeus, it is passing strange
    That here this day should on the dunghill lie.
He for his beauty seemeth fit to range
    Both field and forest; but this know not I,
    Whether his fleetness with his form may vie
Or he the nature of those dogs partake
    Nursed at the table of some chieftain high,
And men preserve them for their beauty's sake'.
Then, O Eumaeus, swineherd, thou did'st answer
        make:

'He to a master that hath died afar
    Pertaineth. Were he what in years of old
Odysseus left him, when he went to war,
    Thou should'st amazed his strength and
        speed behold.
    No creature whom the forest-deeps enfold
Escaped the prowess of his youthful prime,
    In track so true, and in pursuit so bold.

Now hath he fallen on an evil time,
And his dear lord hath perished in a far off
        clime.
'Nor on his wants the careless women tend;
    For servants, when their lords no longer sway,
Their minds no more to righteous courses bend.
        Half that man's virtue doth Zeus take away,
        Whom he surrenders to the servile day.'
He, having spoken, to the doors came near,
    And to the hall of banquet bent his way.
And upon Argus came the death-fate drear,
    Just having seen Odysseus in the twentieth
        year.

Homer,   9th cent. B.C.
Odyssey.

MADNESS IN DOGS IS DANGEROUS: the treatment for rabies.

Madness in dogs is dangerous to human beings when Sirius, the dog star, is shining, and it is then that it causes hydrophobia. So it is a wise precaution in those days to mix dung, best perhaps that of fowls, in the dog's food, or if the disease has already taken hold, hellebore. But for a bite the only cure is one which was lately revealed in an oracle, the root of the wild or dog rose. Columella states that if, forty days after being whelped, the dog's tail is docked and the end joint bitten off, the tail does not grow again and the dog is not liable to madness.

Pliny the Elder,   23 - 79.
Natural History.

OF ENGLISH DOGGES: a description of the Mastiff.

Some tell of starres th'inflnence straunge,
    Some tell of byrdes which flie in th'ayre,
Some tell of beastes on lond which raunge,
    Some tell of fishe in rivers fayre,
Some tell of serpentes sundry sortes,
    Some tell of plantes the full effect,
Of English dogges I sound reportes,
    Their names and natures I detect,
My forhed is but baulde and bare:
    But yet my bod'ys beutifull,
For pleasaunt flowres in me there are,
    And not so fyne as plentifull:
And though my garden plot so greene,
    Of dogges receave the trampling feete,
Yet is it swept and kept full cleane,
    So that it yeelds a savour sweete.

        Abraham Fleming,
        Of English Dogges.

SMALE HOUNDES HAD SHE.

Of smale houndes had she, that she fedde
With rosted flesh, or milk and wastel-breed,
But sore weep she if oon of hem were deed,
Or if men smoot it with a yerde smerte;
And al was conscience and tendre herte.

Geoffrey Chaucer, 1367-1434.
Canterbury Tales, (Prologue).

The Old English Hound

I ONELY SPEAKE OF DOGGES: a description of
the ideal Mastiff.

But now will I onely speake of Dogges
for the husbands, and keepers both of the house
and the Cattell, and first of the Mastie that
keepeth the house; for this purpose you must
provide you such a one as hath a large and a
mightie body, a great and a shrill voyce, that
both with his barking he may discover, and
with his sight dismay the theefe; yea, being
not seene, with the horror of his voyce put him to
flight. His stature must neither be long nor
short, but well set, his head great, his eyes
sharpe, and fiery, either brown or gray; his
lippes blackish, neither turning up nor hanging
too much downe, his mouth black and wide,
his neather jawe fat, appearing more outward
than his other teeth; his upper teeth even with
his neather, not hanging too much over, sharpe,
and hidden with his lippe. His countenance

like a lion, his brest great and shaghayred,
his shoulders broad, his legges bigge, his
tayle short, his feet very great ; his disposition
must neither be too gentle nor too curst,
that he neither fawne upon a theefe, nor flee
upon his friends, very waking, no gadder
abroad, not lavish of his mouth, barking
without cause ; neither maketh it any matter
though he be not swift, for he is but to fight
at home, and to give warning of the enemie.

Barnaby Googe   1540 - 1594
Fowre Bookes of Husbandry.

SO FYNE A KENNEL OF YONG HOWNDES: James I
thanks Lord Buckingham for his gift

Sweete haive blessing blessing
blessing on my sweete tome badgers hairte
rootes and all his, for breiding me so fyne a
kennel of yong howndes, some of thaime so
faire and well shaped, and some of thaime so
fine prettie litle ones as thaye are worthie to
lye on Steenie and Kates bedde; and all of
thaime runne together in a lumpe, both at
sente and vewe, and God thanke the maister
of the horse, for provyding me such a number of
faire usefull horsis, fitte for my honde; in a
worde I proteste I was never maister of suche
horses and howndes; the beavare will tell you
qwhat fyne running we hadde yesterdaye.
Remember now to take the aire discreitlie and
peece and peece, and for God's sакe and myne,
keepe thyselfe verre warme, especially thy
heade and thy showlders, putte thy parke of
Bewlie to an ende, and love me still and

still, and so God blesse thee and my sweete daughter and god-daughter, to the comforte of thy leave Dade.

James. R.

P.S. Thy olde purveyowe sent thee yesternight six pawtridges and two levrettis.

I ame now going to hawke the pheasant.

James I
letter to lord Buckingham.

PERFUMED DOGS:

From perfumed dogs, monkies, sparrows,
Bildoes and paraquettes,
Good mercy defend us.

Ben Jonson   1573-1637

I WAS A SCHOLAR: John Marston compares
his dogs life with his own.

I was a scholar; seven useful springs
Did I deflower in quotations
Of cross'd opinions 'bout the soul of man:
The more I learnt, the more I learnt to doubt.
Delight, my spaniel, slept, whilst I baused leaves,
Tossed o'er the dunces, pored on the old print
Of titled words: and still my spaniel slept.
Whilst I wasted lamp-oil, bated my flesh,
Shrunk up my veins, and still my spaniel slept,
And still I held converse with Zabarell,
Aquinas, Scotus, and the musty saws
Of antique Donate: still my spaniel slept.
Still on went I; first, an sit anima;
Then, an 'twere mortal. O hold, hold! at that
They're at brawn buffets, fell by the ears, amain
(Pell-mell) together: still my spaniel slept.
Then, whether 'twere corporeal, local, fixt,
Ex traduce; but whether 't had free will
Or no, hot philosophers

Stood bonding factions, all so strongly propt,
I staggered, knew not which was firmer part;
But thought, quoted, read, observed, and pried,
Stuffed noting-books: and still my spaniel slept.
At length he waked, and yawned: and by yon sky
For aught I know, he knew as much as I!

John Marston,   1575 - 1634
A Scholar and his Dog.

WHO CAN COMMAND THEIR EXCELLENCY: Izaak
Walton foresakes angling to comment on hounds.

And for the dogs that we use, who
can commend their excellency to that height
which they deserve? How perfect is the
hound at smelling, who never leaves or
forsakes his first scent, but follows it through
so many changes and varieties of other
scents, even over and in water, and into
the earth! What music doth a pack of
dogs then make to any man, whose heart
and ears are so happy as to be set to the
tune of such instruments! For my Hounds,
I know the language of them, and they
know the language and meaning of one
another, as perfectly as we know the voices
of those with whom we discourse daily.

Izaak Walton,   1593 ~ 1683

BELONGING TO THE KINGS MAJESTY: Charles II advertises for the return of his stolen dog.

A Smooth Black DOG, less than a Greyhound, with white under his breast, belonging to the Kings Majesty, was taken from Whitehal, the eighteenth day of this instant June, or thereabout. If any one can give notice to John Ellis, one of his Majesties Servants, or to his Majesties Backstayrs, shall be well rewarded for their labour.

Mercurius Publicus
June 1660

We must call upon you again for a black Dog, between a Greyhound and a Spaniell, no white about him, only a streak on his brest and his taile a little bob'd. It is his Majesties owne Dog, and doubtless was stolen, for the Dog was not born nor bred in England, and would not forsake his Master! Whosoever finds him may aquaint any at Whitehall, for the Dog was better known at Court than those who stole him.

Will they never leave robbing His Majesty?
must he not keep a Dog? This Dogs place
(though better than some imagine) is the
only place which nobody offers to beg.

Mercurius Publicus.
July 1660.

A DOG THAT HE HATH DO KILL ALL THE CATS.

September 11, 1661.

To Dr Williams who did carry me into his
garden, where he hath abundance of grapes:
and he did show me how a dog that he hath
do kill all the cats that come thither to kill
his pigeons; and do afterwards bury them;
and do it with so much care that they shall
be quite covered; that if the tip of the
tail hangs out, he will take up the cat
again and dig the hole deeper; which is
strange. And he tells me he do believe he
hath killed above an hundred cats.

Samuel Pepys,   1633~1703.

A BRACE OF GREYHOUNDS OF HIS HIGHNESS
PRINCE RUPERT: a plea for the safe
return of lost dogs.

On Wednesday, the Ninth instant
were lost a brace of Greyhounds of his Highness Prince Ruperts, the one a large white
young Dog, with a thick black head, with
a Chain and small Coller; The other a
cole black Dog, with a small Coller. If any
person hath taken them up they are desired
either to send or bring them to his Highness
lodgings in the Stone Gallery at Whitehal,
where they shall be well rewarded for them.

The London Gazette,
October, 1667.

Lost in Deans-yard, Westminster,
on the 26th of October last, a young white
Spaniell about six months old, with a black
head, red eye-browes, and a black spot upon
his back. Lost also about the same time

near Camberwell, a Yorkshire Buckhound,
having black spots upon his back, red ears,
and a wall - eye, and P.R. upon his near
shoulder; both belonging to his Highness
Prince Rupert. If any one can bring them
or tydings of them to Prince Ruperts
lodings in the Stone Gallery at Whitehall
he shall be well rewarded for his pains.

The London Gazette
November 1667.

D   Dog.   d

FIRST LET THE KENNEL BE THE HUNTSMAN'S CARE
the incomparable Somerville describes kennel
management.

First let the kennel be the huntsman's care,
Upon some little eminence erect,
And fronting to the ruddy dawn; its courts
On either hand wide op'ning to receive
The sun's all cheering beams, when mild he shines,
And gilds the mountain tops. For much the pack
(Rous'd from their dark alcoves) delight to stretch,
And bask, in his invigorating ray:
Warm'd by the streaming light and merry lark,
Forth rush the jolly clan; with tuneful throats
They carol loud, and in grand chorus join'd
Salute the new-born day. For not alone
The vegetable world, but men and brutes
Own his reviving influence, and joy
At his approach. Fountain of light! if chance
Some envious cloud veil thy refulgent brow,
In vain the Muses aid; untouch'd, unstrung,
Lies my mute harp, and thy desponding bard
Sits darkly musing o'er th' unfinish'd lay.

Let no Corinthian pillars prop the dome,
A vain expense, on charitable deeds

Better dispos'd, to clothe the tatter'd wretch
Who shrinks beneath the blast, to feed the poor
Pinch'd with afflictive want : for use, not state,
Gracefully plain, let each apartment rise.
O'er all let cleanliness preside, no scraps
Bestrew the pavement, and no half-pick'd bones,
To kindle fierce debate, or to disgust
That nicer sense, on which the sportsman's hope
And all his future triumphs must depend.
Soon as the growling pack with eager joy
Have lapp'd their smoking viands, morn or eve,
From the full cistern lead the ductile streams,
To wash thy court well-pav'd; nor spare thy pains,
For much to health will cleanliness avail.
Seek'st thou for hounds to climb the rocky steep,
And brush th' entangled covert, whose nice scent
O'er greasy fallows and frequented roads
Can pick the dubious way? Banish far off
Each noisome stench, let no offensive smell
Invade thy wide enclosure, but admit
The nitrous air and purifying breeze.

Water and shade no less demand thy care:
In a large square th' adjacent field enclose,
There plant in equal ranks the spreading elm,
Or fragrant lime; most happy thy design,
If, at the bottom of thy spacious court,
A large canal, fed by the crystal brook,
From its transparent bosom shall reflect
Thy downward structure and inverted grove.
Here, when the sun's too potent gleams annoy
The crowded kennel, and the drooping pack,
Restless and faint, loll their unmoisten'd tongues,
And drop their feeble tails, to cooler shades
Lead forth the panting tribe; soon shalt thou
                                        find
The cordial breeze their fainting hearts revive:
Tumultuous soon they plunge into the stream,
There lave their reeking sides, with greedy joy
Gulp down the flying wave, this way and that
From shore to shore they swim, while clamour
                                        loud
And wild uproar torments the troubled flood:
Then on the sunny bank they roll and stretch

Their dripping limbs, or else in wanton rings
Coursing around, pursuing and pursued,
The merry multitude disporting play.

But here with watchful and observant eye
Attend their frolics, which too often end
In bloody broils and death. High o'er thy head
Wave thy resounding whip, and with a voice
Fierce-menacing o'er-rule the stern debate,
And quench their kindling rage; for oft in sport
Begun, combat ensues, growling they snarl,
Then, on their haunches rear'd, rampant they seize
Each other's throats, with teeth and claws, in gore
Besmear'd, they wound, they tear, till on the ground,
Panting, half dead the conquer'd champion lies:
Then sudden all the base, ignoble crowd
Loud clam'ring seize the helpless worried wretch,
And, thirsting for his blood, drag diff'rent ways
His mangled carcass on th'ensanguin'd plain.
O! breasts of pity void! t'oppress the weak,
To point your vengeance at the friendless head,
And with one mutual cry insult the fallen!

Emblem too just of man's degenerate race.

Others apart by native instinct led,
Knowing instructor! 'mong the ranker grass
Cull each salubrious plant, with bitter juice
Concoctive stor'd, and potent to allay
Each vitious ferment. Thus the hand divine
Of Providence, beneficent and kind
To all his creatures, for the brutes prescribes
A ready remedy, and is himself
Their great physician. Now grown stiff with age,
And many a painful chace, the wise old hound,
Regardless of the frolic pack, attends
His master's side, or slumbers at his ease
Beneath the bending shade; there many a ring
Runs o'er in dreams; now on the doubtful soil
Puzzles perplex'd, or doubles intricate
Cautious unfolds; then wing'd with all his speed
Bounds o'er the lawn to seize his panting prey,
And in imperfect whimp'rings speaks his joy.

A diff'rent hound for ev'ry diff'rent chace

Select with judgement ; nor the tim'rous hare
O'er-match'd destroy, but leave that vile offence
To the mean, murd'rous coursing crew, intent
On blood and spoil. O blast their hopes, just Heav'n!
And all their painful drudgeries repay
With disappointment and severe remorse.
But husband thou thy pleasures, and give scope
To all her subtle play : by nature led,
A thousand shifts she tries; t'unravel these
Th'industrious beagle twists his waving tail,
Thro' all her labyrinths pursues, and rings
Her doleful knell. See there with count'nance blithe,
And with a courtly grin, the fawning hound
Salutes thee cow'ring, his wide op'ning nose
Upward he curls, and his large sloe-black eyes
Melt in soft blandishments and humble joy;
His glossy skin, or yellow-pied, or blue,
In lights or shades by Nature's pencil drawn,
Reflects the various tints; his ears and legs,
Fleckt here and there, in gay enamel'd pride,
Rival the speckled bard; his rush grown tail
O'er his broad back bends in an ample arch;

On shoulders clean, upright and firm he stands;
His round cat-foot, straight hams, and wide-spread
thighs,
And his low-dropping chest, confess his speed,
His strength, his wind, or on the steepy hill,
Or far extended plain; in ev'ry part
So well proportion'd, that the nicer skill
Of Phidias himself can't blame thy choice
Of such compose thy pack, But here a mean
Observe, nor the large hound prefer, of size
Gigantic; he in the thick-woven covert
Painfully tugs, or in the thorny brake
Torn and embarrass'd bleeds: but if too small,
The pigmy brood in ev'ry furrow swims;
Moil'd in the clogging clay, panting they lag
Behind inglorious; or else shivering creep
Benum'd and faint beneath the shelt'ring thorn.
For hounds of middle size, active and strong,
Will better answer all thy various ends,
And crown thy pleasing labours with success.

PROPAGATE THEIR KIND : Somerville on breeding and rearing.

The prudent huntsman, therefore, will supply
With annual large recruits his broken pack,
And propagate their kind: as from the root
Fresh scions still spring forth, and daily yield
New blooming honours to the parent-tree.
Far shall his pack be fam'd, far sought his breed,
And princes at their tables feast those hands
His hand presents, an acceptable boon.

Ere yet the sun thro' the bright ram has urg'd
His steepy course, or mother Earth unbound
Her frozen bosom to the western gale;
When feather'd troops, their social leagues dissolv'd,
Select their mates, and on the leafless elm
The noisy rook builds high her wicker nest;
Mark well the wanton females of thy pack,
That curl their taper tails, and frisking court
Their piebald mates enamour'd; their red eyes
Flash fires impure; nor rest nor food they take,
Goaded by furious love. In sep'rate cells
Confine them now, lest bloody civil wars
Annoy thy peaceful state. If left at large,

The growling rivals in dread battle join,
And rude encounter. On Scamander's streams
Heroes of old with far less fury fought
For the bright Spartan dame, their valour's prize.
Mangled and torn thy fav'rite hounds shall lie,
Stretch'd on the ground; thy kennel shall appear
A field of blood: like some unhappy town
In civil broils confus'd, while discord shakes
Her bloody scourge aloft, fierce parties rage,
Staining their impious hands in mutual death.
And still the best belov'd and bravest fall:
Such are the dire effects of lawless love.

Huntsman! these ills by timely prudent care
Prevent; for ev'ry longing dame select
Some happy paramour; to him alone
In leagues connubial join. Consider well
His lineage; what his fathers did of old,
Chiefs of the pack, and first to climb the rock,
Or plunge into the deep, or thread the brake
With thorns sharp-pointed, plash'd, and briars
                                    inwoven.

Observe with care his shape, sort, colour, size.
Nor will sagacious huntsmen less regard
His inward habits; the vain babbler shun,
Ever loquacious, ever in the wrong.
His foolish offspring shall offend thy ears
With false alarms, and loud impertinence.
Nor less the shifting cur avoid, that breaks
Illusive from the pack; to the next hedge
Devious he strays, there ev'ry mews he tries;
If haply then he cross the streaming scent,
Away he flies vainglorious, and exults
As of the pack supreme, and in his speed
And strength unrivall'd. Lo! cast far behind
His vex'd associates pant, and lab'ring strain
To climb the steep ascent. Soon as they reach
Th' insulting boaster, his false courage fails,
Behind he lags, doom'd to the fatal noose,
His master's hate, and scorn of all the field.
What can from such be hop'd, but a base brood
Of coward curs, a frantic, vagrant race?

When now the third revolving moon appears,

With sharpen'd horns, above th'horizon's brink,
Without Lucina's aid, expect thy hopes
Are amply crown'd ; short pangs produce to light
The smoking litter, crawling, helpless, blind,
Nature their guide, they seek the pouting teat,
That plenteous streams. Soon as the tender dam
Has form'd them with her tongue, with pleasure
                                          view
The marks of their renown'd progenitors,
Sure pledge of triumphs yet to come. All these
Select with joy ; but to the merc'less flood
Expose the dwindling refuse, nor o'erload
Th'indulgent mother. If thy heart relent,
Unwilling to destroy, a nurse provide,
And to the foster-parent give the care
Of thy superfluous brood; she'll cherish kind
The alien offspring; pleas'd thou shalt behold
Her tenderness and hospitable love.
If frolic now and playful they desert
Their gloomy cell, and on the verdant turf,
With nerves improv'd, pursue the mimic
                                        chase

Coursing around ; unto thy choicest friends
Commit thy valu'd prize : the rustic dames
Shall at thy kennel wait, and in their laps
Receive thy growing hopes, with many a kiss
Caress, and dignify their little charge
With some great title, and resounding name
Of high import. But cautious here observe
To check their youthful ardour, nor permit
The unexperienc'd younker, immature,
Alone to range the woods, or haunt the brakes
Where dodging comes sport : his nerves unstrung,
And strength unequal, the laborious chace
Shall stint his growth, and his rash, forward
                                        youth
Contract such vicious habits, as thy care
And late correction never shall reclaim .

When to full strength arriv'd, mature and bold,
Conduct them to the field; not all at once,
But, as thy cooler prudence shall direct,
Select a few, and form them by degrees
To stricter discipline . With these consort

48

The staunch and steady sages of thy pack,
By long experience vers'd in all the wiles
And subtle doublings of the various chace.
Easy the lesson of the youthful train,
When instinct prompts, and when example guides.

William Somervile,   1675 ~ 1742.
The Chase.

MY FAVOURITE DOG IS A LITTLE ONE : Popes
appreciation of his dog.

      You are to know then, that as it is
likeness that begets affection, so my favourite
dog is a little one, a lean one, and none of the
finest shaped. He is not much spaniel in his
fawning, but has (what might be worth any
man's while to imitate him in) a dumb, surly
sort of kindness that rather shows itself when
he thinks me ill-used by others, than when we
walk quietly or peaceably by ourselves. if
it be the chief point of friendship to comply
with a friend's motions and inclinations,
he possesses this in an eminent degree:
he lies down when I sit, and walks when I
walk, which is more than many good friends
can pretend to.

        Alexander Pope   1688 - 1745.

YOUR COUNTRY REQUIRES A GOOD TERRIER

Your country requires a good terrier. I should prefer the black or white variety : some there are so like a fox, that awkward people frequently mistake one for the other. If you like terriers to run with your pack, large ones, at times, are useful ; but in an earth they do little good, as they cannot always get up to a fox. You had better not enter a young terrier at a badger. Young terriers have not the art of shifting like old ones ; and, should they be good for any thing, most probably will go up boldly to him at once, and get themselves most terribly bitten : for this reason, you should enter them at young foxes when you can.

PETER BECKFORD,   1740 ~ 1809.
Thoughts on Hunting.

THIS TRULY VALUABLE CREATURE: Thomas Bewick, whose incomparable woodcuts illustrate this book, expresses his appreciation of all dogs.

The services of this truly valuable creature have been so eminently useful to the domestic interests of man in all ages, that to give the history of the Dog would be little less than to trace mankind back to their original state of simplicity and freedom, to mark the progress of civilisation through the various changes of the world, and to follow attentively the gradual advancement of that order which placed man at the head of the animal world, and gave him a manifest superiority over every part of the brute creation.

Let us consider for a moment the state of man without the aid of this useful domestic: with what arts shall he oppose the numerous host of foes that surround him on all sides, seeking every opportunity to encroach upon his possessions, to destroy his labours, or endanger his personal safety; or how shall he bring into subjection such as are necessary for his well-being? His utmost vigilance will not be sufficient to secure him from the

rapacity of one, nor his greatest exertions
enable him to overcome the speed of another.
To maintain his independance, to insure his
safety, and to provide for his support, it was
necessary that some one among the animals
should be brought over to his assistance, whose
zeal and fidelity might be depended on: and
where, amidst all the various orders of animated
being, could one be found so entirely adapted to
this purpose? where could one be found so bold,
so tractable, and so obedient as the Dog? To
confirm the truth of these observations, we
need only turn our attention to the present
condition of those nations not yet emerged from
a state of barbarism, where the uses of the
Dog are but little known or attended to, and
we shall find that they lead a precarious and
wretched life of perpetual warfare with still
more savage inhabitants of the forest, with
which they are obliged to dispute the possession
of their uncultivated fields, and not
unfrequently to divide with them the fruits of

their labours. Hence we may conclude, that
the attention of mankind, in the earliest ages,
would be engaged in training and rendering
this animal subservient to the important
purposes of domestic utility; and the result
of this art has been the conquest and
peaceable possession of the earth.

Of all animals, the Dog seems most
susceptible of change, and most easily modified
by difference of climate, food, and education;
not only the figure of his body, but his faculties,
habits, and dispositions, vary in a surprising
manner: nothing appears constant in them
but their internal conformation, which is alike
in all; in every other respect, they are very
dissimilar: they vary in size, in figure, in
the length of the nose and shape of the head,
in the length and direction of the ears and
tail, in the colour, quality, and quantity
of the hair, and c. To enumerate the
different kinds, or mark the discriminations
by which each is distinguished, would be a

task as fruitless as it would be impossible;
to account for this wonderful variety, or
investigate the character of the primitive
stock from which they have sprung, would
be equally vain. Of this only we are certain,
that, in every age, Dogs have been found
possessed of qualities most admirably adapted
for the various purposes to which they have
been from time to time applied. We have seen,
in the history of the Cow and the Sheep, that
those animals which have been long under
the management of man, never preserve
the stamp of nature in its original purity.
In wild animals, which still enjoy their
natural freedom from restraint, and have
the independent choice of food and climate,
this impression is still faithfully preserved;
but those which man has subdued, transported
from climate to climate, changed their food,
habits and manner of living, must necessarily
have suffered the greatest alterations in their
form; and as the Dog, of all other domestic

animals, is most accustomed to this influence,
is endowed with dispositions the most docile
and obedient, is susceptible of every impression,
and submissive to every restraint, we need not
wonder that he should be subject to the
greatest variety. To an attentive observer of
the canine race, it is truly wonderful and
curious to observe the rapid changes and
singular combinations of forms, arising from
promiscuous intercourse, which every where
present themselves: they appear in endless
succession, and seem more like the effect of
whimsical caprice than the regular and
uniform production of Nature, rendering

every idea of a systematic arrangement
dubions and problematical ; but in whatever
light we consider the various mixtures
which at present abound, we may fairly
presume, that the services of the shepherd's
Dog would be first required in maintaining
and preserving the superiority of man over
those animals which were destined for his
support

Thomas Bewick,   1753~1828
A General History of Quadrupeds.

A VERY DISAGREEABLE BROTHER SPORTSMAN :
Cobbett thinks more of gundogs than of their
masters.

A professed shot is, almost always, a
very disagreeable brother sportsman. He must, in
the first place, have a head rather of the emptiest
to pride himself upon so poor a talent. Then he is
always out of temper, if the game fail, or if he
miss it. He never participates in that great
delight which all sensible men enjoy at be-
holding the beautiful action, the docility, the
zeal, the wonderful sagacity of the pointer and
the setter. He is always thinking about himself;
always anxious to surpass his companions. I
remember that, once, Ewing and I had lost our
dog. We were in a wood, and the dog had gone out
and found a covey in a wheat stubble joining the
wood. We had been whistling and calling him
for, perhaps, half an hour or more. When we
came out of the wood we saw him pointing with
one foot up; and soon after, he, keeping his

foot and body unmoved, gently turned round his head towards the spot where he heard us, as if to bid us come on, and, when he saw that we saw him, turned his head back again. I was so delighted that I stopped to look with admiration. Ewing, astonished at my want of alacrity, pushed on, shot one of the partridges, and thought no more about the conduct of the dog than if the sagacious creature had had nothing at all to do with the matter.

William Cobbett   1762 -1835
Rural Rides

DOES HIS TAIL WAG HORIZONTALLY OR VERTICALLY?

Excuse my anxiety - but how is Dash? -
(I should have asked if Mrs Patmore kept her rules,
and was improving - but Dash came uppermost.
The order of our thoughts should be the order of our
writing). Goes he muzzled or aperto ore ? are his
intellects sound, or does he wander a little in his
conversation ? you cannot be too careful to
watch the first symptoms of incoherence. The
first illogical snarl he makes, to St. Luke's with
him! All the dogs here are going mad, if you
believe the overseers ; but I protest they seem
to be very rational and collected. But nothing
is so deceitful as mad people to those who are
not used to them. Try him with hot water. If
he won't lick it up, it is a sign he does not
like it. Does his tail wag horizontally or
perpendicularly ? That has decided the fate
of many dogs in Enfield. Is his general depart-
ment cheerful ? I mean when he is pleased -

for otherwise there is no judging. You can't be too careful. Has he bit any of the children yet? If he has, have them shot, and keep him for a curiousity, to see if it has the hydrophobia.

Charles Lamb 1775 – 1834.
letter to P.G. Patmore
Jan 1827.

A ROUGH TERRIER OF THE HILLS: Wordsworth a
long way from the daffodils.

Among the favourites whom it pleased me well
To see again, was one by ancient right
Our inmate, a rough terrier of the hills;
By birth and call of nature pre-ordained
To hunt the badger and unearth the fox
Among the imperious crags, but having been
From youth our own adopted, he had passed
Into a gentler service. And when first
The boyish spirit flagged, and day by day
Along my veins I kindled with the stir,
The fermentation and the vernal heat
Of poesy, affecting private shades
Like a sick lover, then the dog was used
To watch me, an attendant and a friend,
Obsequious to my steps early and late,
Though often of such dilatory walk
Tired, and uneasy at the halts I made.
A hundred times when roving high and low,
I have been harassed with the toil of verse,

Much pains and little progress, and at once
Some lovely image in the song rose up
Full-formed, like Venus rising from the sea;
Then have I darted forwards to let loose
My hand upon his back with stormy joy,
Caressing him again and yet again.
And when at evening on the public way
I sauntered, like a river murmuring
And talking to itself when all things else
Are still, the creature trotted on before;
Such was his custom; but whene'er he met
A passenger approaching, he would turn
To give me timely notice.

William Wordsworth   1770 ~ 1850
The Prelude.

THE BEST DOG I EVER SAW : an extra-ordinary sheepdog.

My dog Sirrah was, beyond all comparison, the best dog I ever saw. He had a somewhat surly temper, disdaining all flattery, and not caring to be caressed; but his attention to my wishes and interests will never be surpassed. When I bought him he was scarcely a year old, and knew so little of herding that he had never turned a sheep in his life; but as he soon discovered that it was his duty to do so, and that it obliged me, I can never forget with what anxiety and eagerness he learned his different evolutions; and when he had once understood a direction, he never forgot or mistook it.

On one night, a large flock of lambs that were under Hogg's care, frightened by something, scampered away in three different directions across the hills, in spite of all he could do. "Sirrah," said he to his dog, "they've all awa'!"

It was growing dark, and which way to go Hogg knew not. But Sirrah had comprehended the whole mischief, and he set off through the darkness to find the fugitives. Hogg and an assistant traversed every neighbouring hill in search of the lambs; but he could see nothing of them, nor could he get any tidings. He would have to return to his master with the doleful tidings that a flock of seven hundred lambs had been wholly lost. But as the morning dawned, and they were sorrowfully turning homeward, they descried a number of lambs at the bottom of a deep ravine, and soon they were rejoiced to see that their own Sirrah was keeping guard over them. They concluded that one of the three parties of runaways had been found, and that the dog was taking care of them. But what was their astonishment when they found, on coming to the spot, that the whole flock was there; that not one lamb of the seven hundred was missing.

How the dog had achieved this, in what way he
had got all the three parties together, was,
says Hogg, " Quite beyond my comprehension.
All I can say is, that I never felt so
grateful to any living creature as I did to my
honest Sirrah that morning."

James Hogg.   1770 - 1835.

AN HONEST CREATURE : a tribute to a dead dog
Here lies poor Nick, an honest creature,
Of faithful, gentle, courteous nature;
A parlour pet unspoiled by favour,
A pattern of good dog behaviour.
Without a wish, without a dream,
Beyond his home and friends at Cheam,
Contentedly through life he trotted
Along the path that fate allotted;
Till Time, his aged body wearing,
Bereaved him of his sight and hearing,
Then laid them down without a pain
To sleep, and never wake again.

Sidney Smith   1771 - 1845

A BONNIE TERRIER THAT, SIR

'A bonnie terrier that, sir – and a fell chield at the vermin I warrant him, that is if he has been weel entered, for it all lies in that.'

'Really, sir,' said Brown, 'his education has been somewhat neglected, and his chief property is being a pleasant companion.'

'Ay, sir, – that's a pity, begging your pardon, – it's a great pity that; beast or body, education should aye be minded.'

Walter Scott,   1771-1832.
Guy Mannering.

The Terrier

MYSTERY OF BLACK AND TAN.

The Duchess, alias all the other names till you come to the Maid of Lorn, is a rough, gnarled, incomparable little bit of a terrier, three parts Dandie - Dinmont, and one part - chiefly in tail and hair - cocker: her father being Lord Rutherford's famous "Dandie", and her mother the daughter of a Skye, and a lighthearted Cocker. The Duchess is about the size and weight of a rabbit; but has a soul as big, as fierce, and as faithful as had Meg Merrilees, with a nose as black as Topsy's; and is herself every bit as game and queer as that delicious imp of darkness and of Mrs. Stowe. Her legs set her long slim body about two inches and a half from the ground, making her very like a huge caterpillar or hairy oobit - her two eyes, dark and full, and her shining nose, being all of her that seems anything but hair. Her tail was a sort of stump, in size and in look very much like a spare fore-leg, stuck in any-

where to be near. Her colour was black above
and a rich brown below, with two dots of tan
above the eyes, which dots are among the
deepest of the mysteries of Black and Tan.

This strange little being I had known
for some years, but had only possessed about a
month. She and her pup (a young lady called
Smoot, which means smolt, a young salmon),
were given me by the widow of an honest and
drunken – as much of the one as of the other –
Edinburgh street-porter, a native of Badenoch,
as a legacy from him and a fee from her for my
attendance on the poor man's deathbed. But my
first sight of the Duchess was years before in
Broughton Street, when I saw her sitting bolt
upright, begging, imploring, with those little
rough fore leggies, and those yearning, beautiful eyes, all the world, or any one, to help
her master, who was lying "mortal" in the
kennel. I raised him, and with the help of a
ragged Samaritan, who was only less drunk
than he, I got Macpherson – he hed from

Glen Truim - home ; the excited doggie trotting off, and looking back eagerly to show us the way. I never again passed the Porters' Stand without speaking to her. After Malcolm's burial I took possession of her ; she escaped to the wretched house, but as her mistress was off to Kingussie, and the door shut, she gave a pitiful howl or two, and was forthwith back at my door, with an impatient, querulous bark. And so this is our second of the four ; and is she not deserving of as many names as any other Duchess, from her of Medina Sidonia downwards ?

A fierier little soul never dwelt in a queerer or stancher body : see her huddled up, and you would think her a bundle of hair, or a bit of old mossy wood, or a slice of heathery turf, with some red soil underneath ; but speak to her, or give her a cat to deal with, be it bigger than herself, and what an incarnation of affection, energy, and fury - what a fell unquenchable little ruffian !

Dr John Brown   1810 ~ 1882.

BUT THE CHICKENS BLOOD IS UP: the young John Brown finds a dog with the courage of Henry Pearce.

When we got to the top of the street, and turned north, we espied a crowd at the Tron church. "A dog-fight!" shouted Bob, and was off; and so was I, both of us all but praying that it might not be over before we got up! and is not this boy-nature? and human nature too? and don't we all wish a house on fire not to be out before we see it? Dogs like fighting; old Isaac says they "delight" in it, and for the best of all reasons and boys are not cruel because they like to see the fight. They see three of the great cardinal virtues of dog and man — courage, endurance, and skill — in intense action. This is very different from a love of making dogs fight, and enjoying, and aggravating, and making gain by their pluck. A boy — be he ever so fond himself of fighting, if he be a good boy, hates and despises all this, but be he a good boy, hates and despises all this, but he would have run off with Bob and me fast enough: it is a

natural, and a not wicked interest, that all
boys and men have in witnessing intense
energy in action.

Does any curious and finely -
ignorant woman wish to know, how Bob's
eye at a glance announced a dog-fight to
his brain? He did not, he could not see the
dogs fighting; it was a flash of an infer-
ence, a rapid induction. The crowd round
a couple of dogs fighting, is a crowd, mas-
culine mainly, with an occasional
active, compassionate woman, fluttering
wildly round the outside, and using her
tongue and her hands freely upon the men,
as so many "brutes;" it is a crowd
annular, compact, and mobile; a crowd
centripetal, having its eyes and its heads
all bent downwards and inwards, to one
common focus.

Well, Bob and I are up, and find
it is not over: a small, thoroughbred,
white bull-terrier, is busy throttling a

large shepherd's dog, unaccustomed to war,
but not to be trifled with. They are hard at
it; the scientific little fellow doing his work
in great style, his pastoral enemy fighting
wildly, but with the sharpest of teeth and a
great courage. Science and breeding, however, soon took their own; the Game Chicken,
as the premature Bob called him, working
his way up, took his final grip of poor
Yarrow's throat, — and he lay gasping and
done for. His master, a brown, handsome,
big young shepherd from Tweedsmuir, would
have liked to have knocked down any man,
"drunk up Esil, or eaten a crocodile," for
that part, if he had a chance : it was no
use kicking the little dog; that would only
make him hold the closer. Many were the
means shouted out in mouthfuls, of the
best possible ways of ending it. "Water!"
but there was none near, and many
shouted for it who might have got it from
the well at Blackfriars Wynd. "Bite the

tail!" and a large, vague, benevolent, middle-aged man, more anxious than wise, with some struggle got the bushy end of Yarrow's tail in his ample mouth, and bit it with all his might. This was more than enough for the much-enduring, much-perspiring shepherd, who, with a gleam of joy over his broad visage, delivered a terrific facer upon our large, vague, benevolent, middle-aged friend, — who went down like a shot.

Still the Chicken holds; death not far off. "Snuff! a pinch of snuff!" observed sharply a calm, highly-dressed young buck, with an eye-glass in his eye. "Snuff, indeed!" growled the angry crowd, affronted and glaring. "Snuff! a pinch of snuff!" again observes the buck, but with more urgency; whereon were produced several open boxes, and from a mull which may have been at Culloden, he took a pinch, knelt down, and presented it to the nose of the Chicken. The laws of physiol-

ogy and of snuff take their course; the
Chicken sneezes, and Yarrow is free!

The young pastoral giant stalks
off with Yarrow in his arms, — comforting
him.

But the Chicken's blood is up, and
his soul unsatisfied; he grips the first dog
he meets, but discovering she is not a dog,
in Homeric phrase, he makes a brief sort
of amende, and is off; down Niddry Street
he goes, bent on mischief; up the Cowgate
like an arrow — Bob and I, and our small
men, panting behind.

There, under the large arch of the
South Bridge, is a huge mastiff, sauntering
down the middle of the causeway, as if
with his hands in his pockets: he is old,
grey, brindled; as big as a little Highland
bull, and has the Shakesperian dewlaps
shaking as he goes.

The Chicken makes straight at
him, and fastens on his throat. To our

astonishment, the great creature does
nothing but stand still, hold himself up,
and roar — yes, roar; a long, serious,
remonstrative roar. How is this? Bob and
I are up to them. He is muzzled! The bailies
had proclaimed a general muzzling, and his
master, studying strength and economy
mainly, had encompassed his huge jaws
in a home-made apparatus, constructed
out of the leather of some ancient breechin.
His mouth was open as far as it could;
his lips curled up in a rage — a sort of
terrible grin; his teeth gleaming, ready,
from out the darkness; the strap across
his mouth tense as a bowstring; his
whole frame stiff with indignation and
surprise; his roar asking us all round,
"Did you ever see the like of this?" He
looked a statue of anger and astonishment,
done in Aberdeen granite.

We soon had a crowd: the Chicken
held on. "A knife!" cried Bob; and a

cobbler gave him his knife: you know the
kind of knife, worn away obliquely to a
point, and always keen. I put its edge to
the tense leather; it ran before it; and
then! one sudden jerk of that enormous head,
a sort of dirty mist about his mouth, no
noise, — and the bright and fierce little
fellow is dropped, limp, and dead. A solemn
pause; this was more than any of us had
bargained for. I turned the little fellow over,
and saw he was quite dead: the mastiff had
taken him by the small of the back like a
rat, and broken it.

He looked down at his victim appeased,
ashamed, and amazed; snuffed him all over,
stared at him, and taking a sudden thought,
turned round and trotted off. Bob took the dead
dog up, and said "John, we'll bury him after
tea." "Yes," said I; and was off after the
Mastiff. He made up the Cowgate at a rapid
swing: he had forgotten some engagement.
He turned up the Candlemaker Row, and stopped

at the Harrow Inn.

There was a carrier's cart ready to start, and a keen, thin, impatient, black-avised little man, his hand at his grey horse's head, looking about angrily for something. "Rab, ye thief!" said he, aiming a kick at my great friend, who drew cringing up, and avoiding the heavy shoe with more agility than dignity, and watching his master's eye, slunk dismayed under the cart, - his ears down, and as much as he had of tail down too.

What a man this must be - thought I - to whom my tremendous hero turns tail! The carrier saw the muzzle hanging, cut and useless, from his neck, and I eagerly told him the story, which Bob and I always, thought, and still think, Homer, or King David, or Sir Walter, alone were worthy to rehearse. The severe little man was mitigated, and condescended to say, "Rab, my man, puir Rabbie," - whereupon the stump of a tail rose up, the ears were cocked, the eyes filled,

and were comforted; the two friends were recon-
ciled. "Hupp!" and a stroke of the whip were
given to Jess; and off went the three.

Bob and I buried the Game Chicken
that night (we hadn't much of a tea) in the
back-green of his house, in Melville Street,
No 17, with considerable gravity and silence;
and being at the time in the Iliad, and,
like all boys, Trojans, we called him, of
course, Hector.

Dr John Brown,   1810 ~ 1882.
Rab and his Friends.

I KNOW THEM NOW:

Assheton - Smith's affinity with his hounds.

Nor was Mr Smith in any way sparing
of expense in securing the very best blood for his pack.
In addition to Sir R. Sutton's hounds, he bought those
belonging to Sir Thomas Boughey, and, later, the pack
of the Duke of Grafton. In particular he prized most
highly the stock of Mr. Warde, and, as a proof of this,
on one occasion he deputed Mr. F— to offer Mr
Horlock, who had purchased Mr Warde's pack for
£2,000, 1,000 guineas for twenty couples, which Mr
Smith was to pick out from the kennel, without
any other aid to guide him than his own well-
practised eye, in making the selection.

One of the most surprising, and at the
same time interesting, scenes to witness was the
"fascination" he seemed to possess over hounds,
and the strong attachment they always evinced
towards their master. "I recollect," relates one
of his friends, "his once having out five couples
of drafts whom he had never seen before. Sharp,
his kennel huntsman at that time, gave him
their names written down; he then called each
hound separately, and after giving him a

piece of bread, returned the list to the huntsman,
saying, "I know them now ; and so they did him."
On other occasions when the fixture was "Dare
Hill", and the hounds were awaiting his arrival,
Dick Burton used to say, "Master is coming I
perceive by the hounds;" and this, too, long before
he made his appearance. When he came within
three hundred yards, no huntsman or whip in
the world could have stopped the pack from
bounding to meet him. In the morning when let
loose from the kennel, they would rush to his
study window or to the hall door, and stand there
till he came out.

But we must not omit to make
particular mention here of some of his especial
favourites in the kennel at different periods.

Conspicuous among these stands
Solyman, a very fine and large grey hound;
indeed, Nimrod says he was the largest ever
bred in England, standing twenty-seven inches
high, and with bone equal to many ponies. Mr.
Smith was fond of remarking that he would

as soon take this hound's word about a fox as
any man's in England. This saying is like what
Mr. Osbaldeston said of his horse Vaulter, that he
never told a lie in his life. Solyman had, however,
his peculiar days (like other dogs), and sometimes
would do very little. Another great favourite was
Vanquisher, from Sir R. Sutton's kennel, a
beautiful hound, who always kept close to his
master's horse, never drawing before the fox was
found, and then continuing close to the fox till
he was killed. Next comes Trimmer, a grey fine-
shaped hound, also from the same kennel. This
hound, he used to say, was the most perfect and
complete in all his good qualities, such as
finding, hunting, and chasing, of any hound he
ever rode after. Trimbush was another
especial favourite; and Nigel, not unlike in
size and colour (black-pied) to Trimbush,
was equally valued. Nigel always showed the
greatest animation, even when very old,
directly a fox was afoot. He seemed to undergo
a sudden metamorphosis at once from age to

youth, and became full of life and spirit.
Rifleman was also the double favourite both of
the master and mistress, and had almost the
priviledges of a parlour bowder.

Towards the end of the squire's
hunting career, Commoner, Conqueror, Flamer,
and Lexicon invariably went out when-ever he
joined the field. He said it cheered him to see
their old honest faces, although their day for
affording sport was over. There is always, he
said, a gravity and importance of demeanor in
the countenance of a good hound, as if he
knew his superiority over the rest of the
canine species. He was very careful in not
speaking to them when they were at fault, so as
to draw their attention off their work, for, like
Beckford, he could then see an expression of
rebuke in their faces, as much as to say, "what
do you want? let me alone." One of the old
hounds still remains (1860), the patriarch of
the pack, and as finely shaped a foxhound and
as good a one as ever man rode after. This is

old Nelson, well worthy of the name he bears. On
the first day he came, he singled out Mr. Smith,
attached himself to him, and ever afterwards
was the first to salute him when he entered the
field. He had belonged to the Duke of Rutland, and
was of the same size as many of the best hounds
in the pack; in fact, a perfect model of a foxhound, answering in every way to Mr. Meynell's
well-known description — "short back, open
bosom, straight legs, and compact feet;" and
to that by Beckford, equally familiar to
sportsmen, "Let his legs be straight as arrows,
his feet round and not too large, his chest deep
and back broad, his head small, his neck thin,
his tail thick and bushy; if he carries it well,
so much the better." Yet notwithstanding
Beckford, than whom there cannot be better
authority, for his work may be said to be
the fox-hunter's text book, speaks of a thin
neck as recommending a hound, Mr. Smith
used to like "throaty hounds," for he said "that
by getting rid of the throat, the nose goes

along with it, for a throaty hound has invariably a good nose."

It may not be out of place here to describe the animated and interesting scene which invariably occurred when the squire joined his hounds at the meet. Directly he appeared, every hound rushed towards him, and if ever there was a hearty welcome given to man by "dumb animals", theirs was that welcome. It could not be said, however, to be given by "dumb animals", for each hound had a peculiar winning note of its own to express its joy, and no one could for a moment doubt the reciprocal delight both of master and hounds. This was the more singular as Mr. Smith never fed his hounds in the kennel, but, directly the hunting was over for the day, he mounted his hack and galloped home, while hounds returned quietly with the whippers-in.

Sir J. Eardley-Wilmot 1811 - 1892
The Reminiscences of a Foxhunter.

ON SEPARATING FIERCE DOGS FROM INFERIOR ANIMALS.

To the Editor of the Sporting Magazine,

Sir,

Having had an opportunity yesterday of trying an experiment of which I had previously heard spoken, I hasten to communicate the result to your readers, as, though doubtlessly known to some, it may yet be information to many.

On my return home, through Great Surrey-street, I observed a great crowd assembled below the church - which, by the bye, is so common, that, it is well known, the most trifling circumstance will draw a host together - and my curiosity being equally excited, I made towards the spot, and found a sheep under the fangs of a bulldog, which had seized the poor animal by the neck, and fairly pinned it to the ground. The more the dog was beaten the tighter he seemed to retain his hold; and I must do his master the justice to say - whether from fear of the loss of the sheep, or from apprehension of coming under Mr. Martin's Act, I can't tell - he did all in his power to release the poor animal from his fangs. I was more fortunate : for, first desiring the man to take hold of his tail to draw him off when I should have separated them - to prevent his seizing my hand - I took a large pinch of snuff in my fore fingers from my box, and forced it up the dog's nostrils, when he almost instantly let go, shook his head, snuffled, and decamped.

When I first proposed the experiment, I was completely laughed at ; but, nothing daunted by the sneers and hootings of the by-standers, I proceeded ; and on releasing the animal from its fierce assailant, I assure you, that Kean himself, in his most able delineation of character, never got more applause than I received from the assembled multitude.

This, I repeat, may be worth knowing. to those who are unacquainted with so simple and harmless an expedient - as I have frequently seen cruelty exercised in the endeavour to separate dogs of this description which had seized one of inferior breed: and if you think it worthy of notice, it is at the service of your numerous friends and sub-scribers.

  I am, Sir, & c.

  A Snuff - Taker.

October 10, 1825.

  P.S. A second experiment has had a similar result.

TERRIERS

REPLIES TO AN INQUIRY

To the Editor of the Sporting Magazine
Sir,

In your last excellent Number your correspondent A CUB inquires "where the best terriers are to be got?" Suppose I had asked you, Sir, the same question, in regard to sheep or horses, would you not have said, what description do you want? If NIMROD, and not this correspondent, had made the inquiry, I should instantly have imagined he meant a hunter; but CUB, as I am ignorant of the probable bent of his thoughts, is too explicit to be understood.

"— Si brevis esse laboro
Obscurus fio."

Your correspondent may be a dog-fighter, and he may be on the look-out for a dog of sixty pounds weight; or he may be in search of a delicate small terrier to present to a fair lady. The descriptions of animal,

in either of these cases, differ so widely in
properties and appearance, I must beg a
more defined representation of the animal
wished for, before I can venture to recommend
any particular breed.

About fifty years ago I was given
a terrier bitch, named Fury, which was
brought from Belvoir Castle by my old school-
fellow Bob T——. Her progeny was so much
prized, Sir William T—— offered fifty guineas
for one of them. The colour of this daughter
of Fury's was black tan, ticked so very
regularly with white, the coat seemed as it
were frosted; and her shape was perfect.
This breed has been preserved to the present
time. A descendant of this same Fury (I
mention it with horror) was worried to
death in consequence of negligence, by a
bull dog, a few months ago. He died true
game, as he had ever shewn himself to be.

To mark more forcibly how nec-
essary it is to describe the sort of terrier

wanted, I will only mention that I have
perhaps the very best fighting terrier, of her
weight, in England. I have also a favorite,
which will not fight at all, but is a capital
rat - catcher. I have, more-over, of another
sort, a slender ill formed terrier, which will
attack and subdue anything in the shape
of vermin. Also another, of another sort - for
I have terriers of various breeds - which will
engage in any broil or battle with any living
creature. I possess, in addition to these, a
small long- backed duck - legged animal, of the
Scotch breed, which scarcely bears the resemblance of the canine species. Will you then
wonder, Sir, at my asking what sort of
terrier does your correspondent want?
Terriers of the present day are seldom free
from a cross of the bull breed, or a cross
with the cur. By the way — the cross-bred
animals of all descriptions are the best,
generally speaking, for use ; but a terrier's
pedigree should be unstained if the breed is to

be continued.

I have entered a little into detail, to give your correspondent an opportunity of seeking in such a manner that he may find.

I remain, Sir,

REYNARD.

P.S. You may hear from me again soon, to enable you to correct a slight error or two in your last Number.

NOT BITTEN, ARE YOU? Heathcliff's dogs seem to share his disposition.

I took a seat at the end of the hearth
-stone opposite that towards which my land-
lord advanced, and filled up an interval of
silence by attempting to caress the canine
mother, who had left her nursery, and was
sneaking wolfishly to the back of my legs, her
lip curled up, and her white teeth watering for
a snatch. My caress provoked a long, guttural
snarl.

"You'd better let the dog alone,"
growled Mr. Heathcliff in unison, checking
fiercer demonstrations with a punch of his
foot. "She's not accustomed to be spoiled - not
kept as a pet." Then, striding to a side door,
he shouted again, "Joseph!"

Joseph mumbled indistinctly in the
depths of the cellar, but gave no intimation
of ascending; so his master dived down to him,
leaving me vis-a-vis the ruffianly bitch
and a pair of grim, shaggy sheepdogs, who
shared with her a jealous guardianship over
all my movements. Not anxious to come in

contact with their fangs, I sat still; but, imagining they would scarcely understand tacit insults, I unfortunately indulged in winking and making faces at the trio, and some turn of my physiognomy so irritated madam, that she suddenly broke into a fury and leaped on my knees. I flung her back, and hastened to interpose the table between us. This proceeding roused the whole hive; half a dozen four-footed fiends, of various sizes and ages, issued from hidden dens to the common centre. I felt my heels and coat-laps peculiar subjects of assault; and parrying off the larger combatants as effectually as I could with the poker, I was constrained to demand, aloud, assistance from some of the household in re-establishing peace.

    Mr. Heathcliff and his man climbed the cellar steps with vexatious phlegm: I don't think they moved one second faster than usual, though the hearth was

an absolute tempest of worrying and yelping.
Happily, an inhabitant of the kitchen made
more despatch : a lusty dame, with tucked-up
gown, bare arms, and fire-flushed cheeks,
rushed into the midst of us flourishing a
frying-pan - and used that weapon, and
her tongue, to such purpose, that the storm
subsided magically, and she only remained,
heaving like a sea after a high wind, when
her master entered on the scene.

" What the devil is the matter?" he
asked, eyeing me in a manner that I could
ill endure after this inhospitable treatment.

" What the devil, indeed !" I
muttered. " The herd of possessed swine could
have had no worse spirits in them than
those animals of yours, sir. You might as
well leave a stranger with a brood of tigers!"

"They won't meddle with persons who
touch nothing," he remarked, putting the
bottle before me, and restoring the displaced
table. " The dogs do right to be vigilant. Take

a glass of wine ?"

"No, thank you."

"Not bitten, are you ?"

"If I had been, I would have set my signet on the biter."

Heathcliff's countenance relaxed into a grin.

"Come, come," he said, "you are flurried, Mr. Lockwood. Here, take a little wine. Guests are so exceedingly rare in this house that I and my dogs, I am willing to own, hardly know how to receive them. Your health, sir !"

Emily Brontë   1818 ~ 1848.
Wuthering Heights.

STRAINING AT THE SLIPS : William Scropes
classic description of deerhounds coursing red
deer in the traditional manner.

No time was to be lost : the whole party immediately moved forward in silent and breathless expectation, with the dogs in front, straining at the slips ; and on our reaching the top of the hillock, we got a full view of the noble stag, who, having heard our footsteps, had sprung to his legs, and was staring us full in the face, at the distance of about sixty yards.

The dogs were slipped ; a general halloo burst from the whole party, and the stag wheeling round, set off at full speed, with Bruskar and Bran straining after him.

The brown figure of the deer, with his noble antlers laid back, contrasted with the light colour of the dogs stretching along the dark heath, presented one of the most exciting scenes that it is possible to imagine.

The deer's first attempt was to gain some rising ground to the left of the spot where he stood, and rather behind us ; but, being closely pursued by the dogs, he soon found that his only safety was in speed ; and (as a deer does not run well up hill, nor like a roe, straight down hill), on the dogs approaching him, he turned, and almost retraced his footsteps, taking, however, a steeper line of descent than the one by which he ascended. Here the chase became most interesting; the dogs pressed him hard, and the deer, getting confused, found himself suddenly on the brink of a small precipice of about fourteen feet in height, from the bottom of which there sloped a rugged mass of stones. He paused for a moment, as if afraid to take the leap, but the dogs were so close that he had no alternative.

At this time the party were not above 150 yards distant, and most anxiously waited the result, fearing, from the ruggedness of the ground below, that the deer would not survive the leap. They were, however, soon relieved from their anxiety; for though he took the leap, he did so more cunningly than gallantly, dropping himself in the most singular manner, so that his hind legs first reached the broken rocks below: nor were the dogs long in following him; Buskar sprang first, and, extraordinary to relate, did not lose his legs; Bran followed, and, on reaching the ground, performed a complete somerset; he soon, however, recovered his legs; and the chase was continued in an oblique direction down the side of a most rugged and rocky brae, the deer apparently more fresh and nimble than ever, jumping through the rocks like a goat, and the dogs well up, though occasionally receiving the most fearful falls.

From the high position in which we were placed, the chase was visible for nearly half a mile. When some rising ground intercepted our view, we made with all speed for a higher point, and, on reaching it, we could perceive that the dogs, having got upon smooth ground, had gained on the deer, who was still going at speed, and were close up with him. Bran was then leading, and in a few seconds was at his heels, and immediately seized his hock with such a violence of grasp, as seemed in a great measure to paralyse the limb, for the deer's speed was immediately checked. Buskar was not far behind, for soon afterwards passing Bran, he seized the deer by the neck. Notwithstanding the weight of the two dogs which were hanging to him, having the assistance of the slope of the ground, he continued dragging them along at a most extraordinary rate (in defiance of their utmost exertions to detain him), and succeeded more than once in kicking Bran off. But he became at length exhausted; the dogs succeeded in pulling him down, and, though he made several attempts to rise, he never completely regained his legs.

On coming up, we found him perfectly dead.

William Scrope.
The Art of Deer Stalking.

POINTER, HOUSE-DOG AND HORSE TO GUSTAVUS
JAMES :

Mr Sponge goes shooting with Jog in less than the grand manner.

Having cut himself some extremely substantial sandwiches, and filled his 'monkey' full of sherry, our friend Jog slipped out the back way to loosen old Ponto, who acted the triple part of pointer, house-dog, and horse to Gustavus James. He was a great fat, black-and-white brute, with a head like a hat-box, a tail like a clothes-peg, and a back as broad as a well-fed sheep's. The old brute was so frantic at the sight of his master in his green coat, and wide-awake to match, that he jumped and bounced, and barked, and rattled his chain, and set up such yells, that his noise sounded all over the house, and soon brought Mr. Sponge to the scene of action, where our friend stood loading his gun and looking consequential as possible.

"I shall only just take a (puff) stroll over may (wheeze) ter-ri-to-ry," observed Jog, as Mr. Sponge emerged at the back door.

Jog's pace was about two miles and a half an hour, stoppages included, and he

thought it advisable to prepare Mr. Sponge for
the trial. He then shouldered his gun and
waddled away, first over the stile into Farmer
Stiffland's stubble, round which Ponto ranged
in the most riotous, independant way, regardless of Jog's whistles and rates, and the crack
of his little knotty whip. Jog then crossed the
old pasture into Mr. Lowland's turnips, into
which Ponto dashed in the same energetic way,
but these impediments to travelling soon told
on his great buttermilk carcass, and brought
him to a more subdued pace; still, the dog
had a good deal more energy than his master.
Round he went, sniffing and hunting, then
dashing right through the middle of the field,
as if he was out on his own account alone,
and had nothing whatever to do with a
master.

"Why, your dog'll spring all the birds
out of shot," observed Mr. Sponge; and, just as
he spoke, whirr! rose a covey of partridges,
eleven in number, quite at an impossible

distance, but Jog blazed away all the same.

Robert S. Surtees,   1803 ~ 1864
Mr. Sponges Sporting Tour.

A PAROXYSM OF NATURAL INDIGNATION:
Borrow's version of the familiar story of Gelert.

Both Gelert is situated in a valley surrounded by huge hills, the most remarkable of which are Moel Hebog and Cerrig Llan; the former fences it on the south, and the latter, which is quite black and nearly perpendicular, on the east. A small stream rushes through the valley, and sallies forth by a pass at its south-eastern end. The valley is said by some to derive its name of Beddgelert, which signifies the grave of Gelert, from being the burial-place of Gelert, a British saint of the sixth century, to whom Llangeler in Carmarthenshire is believed to have been consecrated, but the popular and most universally received tradition is that it has its name from being the resting-place of a faithful dog

called Celert or Gelert, killed by his master,
the warlike and celebrated Llywelyn ab
Jorwerth, from an unlucky misapprehension.
Though the legend is known to most people,
I shall take the liberty of relating it.

Llewelyn during his contests with
the English had encamped with a few
followers in the valley, and one day departed
with his men on an expedition, leaving his
infant son in a cradle in his tent, under
the care of his hound Gelert, after giving
the child its fill of goat's milk. Whilst he
was absent a wolf from the neighbouring
mountains, in quest of prey, found its way
into the tent, and was about to devour
the child, when the watchful dog interfered,
and after a desperate conflict, in which
the tent was torn down, succeeded in dest-
roying the monster. Llewelyn returning at
evening found the tent on the ground, and
the dog, covered with blood, sitting beside

it. Imagining that the blood with which Gelert was besmeared was that of his own son devoured by the animal to whose care he had confided him, Llewelyn in a paroxysm of natural indignation forthwith transfixed the faithful creature with his spear.

Scarcely, however, had he done so when his ears were startled by the cry of a child from beneath the fallen tent, and hastily removing the canvas he found the child in its cradle, quite uninjured, and the body of an enormous wolf, frightfully torn and mangled, lying near. His breast was now filled with conflicting emotions, joy for the preservation of his son, and grief for the fate of his dog, to whom he forthwith hastened. The poor animal was not quite dead, but presently expired, in the act of licking his master's hand. Llywelyn mourned over him as over a brother, buried him with funeral honours in the valley, and erected a

tomb over him as over a hero. From that
time the valley was called Beth Gelert.

GEORGE BORROW.   1803 ~ 1881.
Wild Wales.

RATS WERE NOT HIS ONLY DIVERSION : Mayhew
describes a poor mans pride and joy.

The man's first anxiety was to show
us that rats were not his only diversion;
and in consequence he took us into the yard
of the house, where in a shed lay a bull-dog,
a bull-bitch, and a litter of pups just a week
old. They did not belong to him, but he said he
did a good deal in the way of curing dogs when
he could get 'em.

After I had satisfied him that I was
not a collector of dog-tax, trying to find out
how many animals he kept, he gave me what
he evidently thought was a 'treat' – a
peep at his bull - dog, which he fetched

from upstairs, and let it jump about the room with a most unpleasant liberty, informing me the while how he had given five pounds for him, and that one of the first pups he got by a bull he had got five pounds for, and that cleared him. 'That Punch' (the bull-dog's name), he said, 'is as quiet as a lamb - wouldn't hurt nobody; I frequently takes him through the streets without a lead. Sartainly he killed a cat the t'other afternoon, but he couldn't help that, 'cause the cat flew at him; though he took it as quietly as a man would a woman in a passion, and only went at her just to save his eyes. But you couldn't - easy get him off, master, when he once got a holt. He was a good one for rats, and, he believed, the staunchest and trickiest dog in London.'

Henry Mayhew,   1812 ~ 1887.
London Labour and the London Poor.

OF CATS' AND DOGS' - MEAT DEALERS.

The supply of food for cats and dogs is far greater than may be generally thought. 'Vy, sir', said one of the dealers to me, 'can you tell me 'ow many people's in London?' On my replying, upwards of two millions; 'I don't know nothing vatever', said my informant, 'about millions, but I think there's a cat to every ten people, aye, and more than that; and so, sir, you can reckon'.

'I must know, for they all knows me, and I sarves about 200 cats and 70 dogs. Mines a middling trade, but some does far better. Some cats has a hap'orth a day, some every other day; werry few can afford a penn'orth, but times is inferior. Dogs is better pay when you've a connection among 'em.'

The cat and dogs'-meat dealers, or 'carriers', as they call themselves, generally purchase the meat at the knackers' (horse-slaughterers') yards.

The carriers then take the meat

round the town, wherever their 'walk' may lie. They sell it to the public at the rate of 2½ d. per lb., and in small pieces, on skewers, at a farthing, a halfpenny, and a penny each. Some carriers will sell as much as a hundred-weight in a day, and about half a hundred-weight is the average quantity disposed of by the carriers in London. Some sell much cheaper than others.

But the trade is much worse now. There are so many at it, they say, that there is barely a living for any. A carrier assured me that he seldom went less than 30, and frequently 40 miles, through the streets every day. The best districts are among the houses of tradesmen, mechanics, and labourers. The coachmen in the mews at the back of the squares are very good customers. 'The work lays thicker there,' said my informant. Old maids are bad, though very plentiful, customers. They cheapen the carriers down so, that they

can scarcely live at the business. 'They
will pay one halfpenny and one another,
and forget that after a day or two.' The cats'
meat dealers generally complain of their
losses from bad debts.

One gentleman has as much as
4 lbs of meat each morning for two Newfound
-land dogs; and there was one woman - a
black - who used to have as much as 16
pennyworth every day. This person used to
get out on the roof of the house and throw it
to the cats on the tiles. By this she brought
so many stray cats round about the neighbourhood, that the parties in the vicinity
complained; it was quite a nuisance. She
would have the meat always brought to
her before ten in the morning, or else she
would send to a shop for it, and between ten
and eleven in the morning the noise and
cries of the hundreds of stray cats attracted
to the spot was 'terrible to hear'. When the
meat was thrown to the cats on the roof,

the riot, and confusion, and fighting, was beyond description. 'A beershop man' I was told, 'was obliged to keep five or six dogs to drive the cats from his walls.'

The generality of the dealers wear a shiny hat, black plush waistcoat and sleeves, a blue apron, corduroy trousers, and a blue and white spotted handkerchief round their necks. Some, indeed, will wear two and three handkerchiefs around their necks, this being fashionable among them.

Henry Mayhew, 1812 ~ 1887.
London Labour and the London Poor.

OF THE FORMER STREET-SELLERS, 'FINDERS', STEALERS, AND RESTORERS OF DOGS.

Before I describe the present condition of the street-trade in dogs, which is principally in spaniels, or in the description well known as lap-dogs, I will give an account of the former condition of the trade, if trade it can properly be called, for the 'finders' and 'stealers' of dogs were the most especial subjects of a parliamentary inquiry, from which I derive the official information on the matter. The Report of the Committee was ordered by the House of Commons to be printed, July 28, 1844.

In their Report the Committee observe, concerning the value of pet dogs:— 'From the evidence of various witnesses it appears, that in one case a spaniel was sold for 105ℓ., and in another, under a sheriff's execution, for 95ℓ. at the hammer; and 50ℓ. or 60ℓ. are not unfrequently given for fancy dogs of first-rate breed and beauty.' The hundred guineas' dog above alluded to was a 'black and tan King Charles's spaniel;' — indeed, Mr. Dowling, the editor of Bell's Life in London, said, in his evidence before the Committee, 'I have known as much as 150 L. given for a dog.' He said afterwards : 'There are certain marks about the eyes and otherwise, which are considered "properties;" and it depends entirely upon the property which a dog possesses as to its value.'

I cannot better show the extent and lucrativeness of this trade, than by citing a list which one of the witnesses before Parliament, Mr. W. Bishop, a gunmaker, delivered in to the Committee, of 'cases in which money had recently been exorted from the owners of dogs by dog-stealers and their confederates.' There is no explanation of the space of time included under the vague term 'recently': but the return shows that 151 ladies and gentlemen had been the victims of dog-stealers or dog-finders, for in this business the words

were, and still are to a degree, synonyms, and
of these 62 had been so victimized in 1843
and in the six months of 1844, from January
to July. The total amount shown by Mr.
Bishop to have been paid for restoration of
stolen dogs was 977£. 4s. 6d., or an average
of 6£.10s. per individual practised upon.

These dog appropriators, as they
found that they could levy contributions not
only on royalty, foreign ambassadors, peers,
courtiers, and ladies of rank, but on public
bodies, and on the dignitaries of the state,
the law, the army, and the church, became
bolder and more expert in their avocations –
a boldness which was encouraged by the
existing law. Prior to the parliamentary
inquiry, dog-stealing was not an indictable
offence. The only mode of punishment for dog-
stealing was by summary conviction, the
penalty being fine or imprisonment; but
Mr. Commissioner Mayne did not know of
any instance of a dog-stealer being sent to

prison in default of payment. Although the
law recognised no property in a dog, the
animal was taxed; and it was complained at
the time that an unhappy lady might have
to pay tax for the full term upon her dog,
perhaps a year and a half after he had
been stolen from her. One old offender, who
stole the Duke of Beaufort's dog, was transported, not for stealing the dog, but his collar.

The difficulty of proving the positive
theft of a dog was extreme. In most cases,
where the man was not seen actually to seize
a dog which could be identified, he escaped
when carried before a magistrate. 'The dog-
stealers,' said Inspector Shackell, 'generally
go two together; they have a piece of liver;
they say it is merely bullock's liver, which
will entice or tame the wildest or savagest
dog which there can be in any yard; they
give it to him, and take him from his chain.
At other times,' continues Mr. Shackell,
'they will go in the street with a little dog,

rubbed over with some sort of stuff, and will
entice valuable dogs away .... If there is a
dog lost or stolen, it is generally known within five or six hours where that dog is, and
they know almost exactly what they can get
for it, so that it is a regular system of plunder.'
Mr. G. White, 'dealer in lions, and tigers, and
all sorts of things,' said of the dog-stealers:
'In turning the corners of streets there are two
or three of them together; one will snatch up
a dog and put into his apron, and the others
will stop the lady and say, "What is the
matter?" and direct the party who has lost
the dog in a contrary direction to that taken.'

In this business were engaged
from 50 to 60 men, half of them actual
stealers of the animals. The others were the
receivers, and the go-betweens or 'restorers.'
The thief kept the dog perhaps for a day or
two at some public-house, and he then took
it to a dog-dealer with whom he was
connected in the way of business. These dealers

carried on a trade in 'honest dogs', as one of the witnesses styled them (meaning dogs honestly acquired), but some of them dealt principally with the dog-stealers. Their depots could not be entered by the police, being private premises, without a search-warrant - and direct evidence was necessary to obtain a search-warrant - and of course a stranger in quest of a stolen dog would not be admitted. Some of the dog-dealers would not purchase or receive dogs known to have been stolen, but others bought and speculated in them. If an advertisement appeared offering a reward for the dog, a negotiation was entered into. If no reward was offered, the owner of the dog, who was always either known or made out, was waited upon by a restorer, who undertook 'to restore the dog if terms could be come to'. A dog belonging to Colonel Fox was once kept six weeks before the thieves would consent to the Colonel's terms. One of the most successful restorers was a shoe-maker, and mixed little with the

actual stealers ; the dog - dealers, however, acted
as restorers frequently enough . If the person
robbed paid a good round sum for the restoration
of a dog, and paid it speedily, the animal was
almost certain to be stolen a second time, and
a higher sum was then demanded. Sometimes
the thieves threatened that if they were any
longer trifled with they would inflict torture on
the dog , or cut its throat . One lady, Miss Brown
of Bolton - street, was so worried by these threats,
and by having twice to redeem her dog, ' that she
has left England,' said Mr. Bishop, ' and I really
do believe for the sake of keeping the dog.' It
does not appear, as far as the evidence shows,
that these threats of torture or death were
ever carried into execution ; some of the
witnesses had merely heard of such things.

Henry Mayhew   1812 ~ 1887.
London Labour and the London Poor.

DOG - STEALING.

These robberies are generally committed by
dog-fanciers and others who confine their
attention to this class of felonies. They are
persons of a low class, dressed variously,
and are frequently followed by women. They
steal fancy dogs ladies are fond of - spaniels,
poodles, and terriers, sporting-dogs, such as
setters and retrievers, and also Newfoundland
dogs. These robberies are generally committed
by men of various ages, but seldom by boys.
Their mode of operation is this: In prowling
over the metropolis, when they see a handsome dog with a lady or gentleman they
follow it and see where the person resides. So
soon as they have ascertained this they
loiter about the house for days with a piece
of liver prepared by a certain process, and
soaked in some ingredient which dogs are
uncommonly fond of. They are so partial to
it they will follow the stranger some distance
in preference to following their master. The

thieves generally carry small pieces of this
to entice the dog away with them, when they
seize hold of it in a convenient place, and
put it into a bag they carry with them.

Another method of decoying dogs is
by having a bitch in heat. When any valuable
dog follows it is picked up and taken home,
when they wait for the reward offered by the
owner to return it, generally from £1 to £5.
The loss of the dog may be advertised in the
Times or other newspapers, or by handbills
circulated over the district, when some
confederate of the thief will negotiate with the
owner for the restoration of the dog. Information
is sent if he will give a certain sum of money,
such as £1, £2 or £5, the dog will be restored,
if not it will be killed. This is done to excite
sympathy.

Some dogs have been known to be
stolen three or four times, and taken back to
their owners by rewards. Sometimes when
they steal dogs they fancy, they keep them

and do not return them to the owner.

There is a class termed dog-receivers, or dog-fanciers, who undertake to return stolen dogs for a consideration. These parties are connected with the thieves, and are what is termed "in the ring", that is, in the ring of thieves. Dogs are frequently restored by agencies of this description. These parties receive dogs and let owners have them back for a certain sum of money, while they receive part of the price shared with the thief.

Dog-stealing is very prevalent, particularly in the West End of the metropolis, and is rather a profitable class of felony. These thieves reside at the Seven Dials, in the neighbourhood of Belgravia, Chelsea, Knightsbridge, and low neighbourhoods, some of them men of mature years.

They frequently pick up dogs in the street when their owners are not near. But their general mode is to loiter about the houses and entice them away in the manner described. Sometimes they belong to the felon class, sometimes not. They are often connected with bird-fanciers, keepers of fighting-dogs, and persons who get up rat matches.

Some of those stolen are sent to Germany, where English dogs are sold at a high price.

Henry Mayhew   1812 ~ 1887.
London Labour and the London Poor
(Those That Will Not Work)

SURPRISING INSTINCT: the sagacity of a Pointer, a tall story.

"Sportsman, sir?" abruptly turning to Mr Winkle.

"A little, sir," replied that gentleman.

"Fine pursuit, sir - fine pursuit - Dog, sir?"

"Not just now," said Mr. Winkle.

"Ah! you should keep dogs - fine animals - sagacious creatures - dog of my own once - Pointer - surprising instinct - out shooting one day - entering inclosure - whistled - dog stopped - whistled again - Ponto - no go : Stock still -

The Spanish Pointer

called him - Ponto, Ponto - wouldn't move - dog transfixed - staring at a board - looked up, saw an inscription - "Gamekeeper has orders to shoot all dogs found in this inclosure" - wouldn't pass it - wonderful dog - valuable dog that - very."

"Singular circumstance that," said Mr. Pickwick, "will you allow me to make a note of it?"

"Certainly, sir, certainly - hundred more anecdotes of the same animal."

Charles Dickens,   1812 ~ 1870.
The Pickwick Papers.

HE AIN'T A LADY'S DOG, YOU KNOW.

'If you'd like to have him, he's at
the door. I brought him on purpose for you. He
ain't a lady's dog, you know,' said Mr. Toots,
'but you won't mind that, will you?'

In fact, Diogenes was at that
moment, as they presently ascertained from
looking down into the street, staring through
the window of a hackney cabriolet, into which,
for conveyance to that spot, he had been
ensnared, on a false pretence of rats among
the straw. Sooth to say, he was as unlike a
lady's dog as dog might be; and in his gruff
anxiety to get out presented an appearance
sufficiently unpromising, as he gave short yelps
out of one side of his mouth, and over balancing
himself by the intensity of every one of these
efforts, tumbled down into the straw, and then
sprang panting up again, putting out his
tongue, as if he had come express to a dispens-
ary to be examined for his health.

But though Diogenes was as ridiculous

a dog as one would meet with on a summer's
day; a blundering, ill - favoured, clumsy, bullet-
headed dog, continually acting on a wrong
idea that there was an enemy in the neighbourhood, whom it was meritorious to bark
at; and though he was far from good-temp-
ered, and certainly was not clever, and had
hair all over his eyes, and a comic nose, and
an inconsistant tail, and a gruff voice; he
was dearer to Florence, in virtue of that parting
remembrance of him, and that request that he
might be taken care of, than the most
valuable and beautiful of his kind. So dear
indeed, was this same ugly Diogenes, and so
welcome to her, that she took the jewelled
hand of Mr Toots and kissed it in gratitude.
And when Diogenes, released, came tearing up
the stairs and bouncing into the room (such
a business as there was first to get him out
of the cabriolet!) dived under all the furniture,
and wound a long iron chain, that dangled
from his neck, round legs of chairs and tables,

and then tugged at it until his eyes became
unnaturally visible, in consequence of their
nearly starting out of his head; and when he
growled at Mr Toots, who affected familiarity;
and went pell-mell at Towlinson, morally
convinced that he was the enemy whom he
had barked at round the corner all his life
and never seen yet; Florence was as pleased
with him as if he had been a miracle of
discretion.

Charles Dickens,   1812 ~ 1870
Dombey and Son.

A SMALL BOLD BREED : Britain's ancient and
hardy breed.

A small bold breed and steady to the game
Next claims the tribute of peculiar fame!
Train'd by the tribes on Britain's wildest shore,
Thence they their title Agasses bore.
Small as the race that useless to their lord
Bask on the hearth and beg about the board,
Crook-limbed and black-eyed, all their frame
appears
Flanked with no flesh and bristled rough with hairs
But shod each foot with hardest claws is seen,
The sole's kind armour on the beaten green;
But fenced each jaw with closest teeth is found,
And death sits instant on th'inflicted wound.
Far o'er the rest he quests the secret prey,
And sees each track wind opening to his ray:
Far o'er the rest he feels each scent that blows
Count the live nerve and thrill along the nose.

John Whitaker.

THE TRUST REPOSED IN YOU WAS SADLY MISDIRECTED: a judge put firmly and none too kindly in his place.

As an exhibitor of Wish Terriers at Ayr yesterday, and as I was very much disappointed with the awards, I feel it a duty to demand an explanation from you for acting in the manner you did. In the dog class you gave Garryford first, which was right enough, provided Garryford had a right to be there, which is very doubtful, he being a champion dog. Were it not that Garryford's new owner is a descendant of 'King Agrippa' he would not have been there, as no gentleman would send a champion dog to compete in such classes. As for Gifford - had it not been that his chain was in Mr Lumsden's left hand, he would not have been looked at, as no man who knows anything about an Wish Terrier would look at him. You gave third to a dog with nothing but legs to look at; whereas Fagan got fourth - a dog that has been first in England before a competant judge. Either you know nothing about an Wish Terrier, or, if you do, it was evident that it was the owner and not the dog, that got the prize.

In the bitch class you placed Randy fourth after being changed from fifth – a bitch that was second at Glasgow in a class of twenty dogs. You put her first at Wishaw and gave nothing to Erin; yesterday you gave Erin second over the same bitch Randy, and made the lame excuse that you did not know Erin – a bitch wide in chest and with a very bad leg, and has a face like a monkey. You told me in the ring that Randy's coat was soft; there was no difference in her coat from Wishaw show. I have bred Fox, Skyes and Irish Terriers before you knew what a dog was. I should like to know how you have the audacity to pose before the public as a judge of Irish Terriers. Did you ever breed or own one? Do you know anything about their points? If you do, the trust reposed in you was sadly misdirected. Do not imagine for a moment that I am going to be sat upon by an amateur like you. I have no objection to other people paying for your education, but I do not intend to do so. I made careful search for you yesterday after

I got my dogs on their benches, for the purpose of
having an explanation from you. You may
consider yourself very lucky I did not find you - and
future exhibitors of Irish Terriers were unfortunate
that I did not - as I would have given you a few
practical hints that you would have remembered
every time you saw an Irish Terrier. However I
will make it my special study to see you on the
subject. Meantime I demand an explanation from
you. I do not intend to speak behind your back,
as you did of me in the ring yesterday, but to
inform you that I intend to write to the 'Stock-
keeper' and other papers on the subject.

You told Mr Lumsden yesterday that you
had made a mess of it - so Mr Lumsden told me.
Well, it is my turn now. An explanation I demand
at once.

David McLachlan
letter to the Editor
Scottish Fancier and Rural Gazette
May 1887.

J Judge

THE LITTLE RED DOG : the ubiquitous feral dog

Sauntering along a lane-like road between Charterhouse Hinton and Woolverton, in the West Country, I spied a small red dog trotting along some distance behind me. He was in the middle of the road, but seeing that he was observed he sheered off to the other side, and when nearly abreast of me paused suspiciously, sniffed the air to get the exact smell, then made a dash past, and after going about twenty or thirty yards full speed, dropped once more into his travelling trot, to vanish from sight at the next bend in the road.

Though alone, I laughed, for he was a very old acquaintance of mine. I knew him well, although he did not know me, and regarding me as a stranger he very naturally associated my appearance with a well-aimed stone or half-brick which had doubtless registered an impression on his small brain. I knew him because he is a common type, widely distributed on the earth; I doubt if there are many countries where you will not meet

him - a degenerate or dwarf variety of the
universal cur, smaller than a fox-terrier
and shorter-legged; the low stature, long body,
small ears, and blunt nose giving him a
somewhat stoaty or even reptilian appearance
among the canines. His red colour is, indeed,
the commonest hue of the common dog, or cur,
wherever found. It is rarely a bright red,
like that of the Irish setter, or any pleasing
shade of red, as in the dingo, the fox, and the
South American maned wolf; it is dull, often
inclining to yellow, sometimes mixed with grey
as in the jackal, sometimes with a dash of
ginger in it. The unbeautiful yellowish-red
is the prevailing hue of the pariah dog. At all
events that is the impression one gets from
the few of the numberless travellers in the
East who have condescended to tell us anything about this low-down animal.

Where the cur or pariah flourishes,
there you are sure to find the small red dog,
and perhaps wonder at his ability to maintain

his existence. He is certainly placed at a great
disadvantage. If he finds or steals a bone, the
first big dog he meets will say to him, "Drop
it!" And he will drop it at once, knowing very
well that if he refuses to do so it will be taken
from him, and his own poor little bones
perhaps get crunched in the process. As
compensation he has, I fancy, a somewhat
quicker intelligence, a subtler cunning. His
brains weigh less by a great deal than those
of the bulldog or a big cur, but - like ladies'
brains compared with men's - they are of a
finer quality.

When I encountered this animal in
the quiet Somerset road, and laughed to see him
and exclaimed mentally, "There he goes, the
same old little red dog, suspicious and sneaky
as ever, and very brisk and busy although his
years must be well-nigh as many as my own,"
I was thinking of the far past, and the sight
of him brought back a memory of one of the
first of the small red dogs I have known

intimately. I was a boy then, and my home was
in the pampas of Buenos Ayres. I had a young
sister, a bright, lively girl, and I remember that
a poor native woman who lived in a smoky
hovel a few miles away was fond of her, and
that she came one day with a present for her
- something precious wrapped up in a shawl -
a little red pup, one of a litter which her own
beloved dog had brought forth. My sister
accepted the present joyfully, for though we
possessed fourteen or fifteen dogs at the time,
these all belonged to the house; they were everybody's and nobody's in particular, and she was
delighted to have one that would be her very own.
It grew into a common red dog, rather better-
looking than most of its kind, having a
bushier tail, longer and brighter-coloured hair,
and a somewhat foxy head and face. In spite
of these good points, we boys never tired of
laughing at her little Reddie, as he was called,
and his intense devotion to his young mistress
and faith in her power to protect him only

made him seem more ludicrous. When we all
walked together on the grass plain, my brother
and I used to think it great fun to separate
Reddie from his mistress by making a sudden
dash, and then hunt him over the turf. Away
he would go, performing a wide circuit, then,
doubling back, would fly to her for safety. She,
stooping and holding out her hands to him,
would wait his coming, and at the end, with
one flying leap, he would land himself in her
arms, almost capsizing her with the force of the
impact, and from that refuge look back
reproachfully at us.

The cunning little ways of the small
red dog were learned later when I came to know
him in the city of Buenos Ayres. Loitering at
the waterside one day, I became aware of an
animal of this kind following me, and no
sooner did he catch my eye than he came up,
wagging, wriggling, and grinning, smiling, so to
speak, all over his body; and I, thinking he
had lost home and friends and touched by his

appeal, allowed him to follow me through the streets to the house of relations where I was staying. I told them I intended keeping the outcast awhile to see what could be done with him. My friends did not welcome him warmly, and they even made some disparaging remarks about little red dogs in general; but they gave him his dinner - a big plateful of meat - which he devoured greedily, and then, very much at home, he stretched himself out on the hearthrug and went fast asleep. When he woke an hour later he jumped up and ran to the hall, and, finding the street-door closed, made a great row, howling and scratching at the panels. I hurried out and opened the door, and out and off he went, without so much as a thank-you. He had found a fool and had succeeded in getting something out of him, and his business with me was ended. There was no hesitation; he was going straight home, and knew his way quite well.

Years afterwards It was a surprise

to me to find that the little red dog was an
inhabitant of London. There was no muzzling
order then, in the 'seventies, and quite a
common sight was the independent dog, usually
a cur, roaming the streets in search of stray
scraps of food. He shared the sparrows' broken
bread; he turned over the rubbish heaps left by
the road-sweepers; he sniffed about areas, on
the look-out for an open dust-bin; and he hung
persistently about the butcher's shop, where a
jealous eye was kept on his movements. These
dogs doubtless had owners, who paid the yearly
tax; but it is probable that in most cases they
found for themselves. Probably, too, the adventur-
ous life of the streets, where carrion was not
too plentiful, had the effect of sharpening their
wits. Here, at all events, I was witness of an
action on the part of a small red dog which
fairly astonished me; that confidence trick
the little Argentine beast had practised on me
was nothing to it.

In Regent Street, of all places, one

bright winter morning, I caught sight of a dog
lying on the pavement close to the wall, hungrily
gnawing at a big beef bone which he had stolen
or picked out of a neighbouring dust-hole. He was
a miserable-looking object, a sort of lurcher,
of a dirty red colour, with ribs showing like the
bars of a grid-iron through his mangy side.
Even in those pre-muzzling days, when we
still had the pariah, it was a little strange
to see him gnawing his bone at that spot,
just by Peter Robinson's, where the broad
pavement was full of shopping ladies; and I
stood still to watch him. Presently a small red
dog came trotting along the pavement from the
direction of the Circus, and catching sight of
the mangy lurcher with the bone he was
instantly struck motionless, and crouching
low as if to make a dash at the other, his tail
stiff, his hair bristling, he continued gazing
for some moments; and then, just when I
thought the rush and struggle was about to
take place, up jumped this little red cur and

rushed back towards the Circus, uttering a
succession of excited shrieky barks. The con-
tagion was irresistible. Off went the lurcher,
furiously barking too, and quickly overtaking
the small dog dashed on and away to the
middle of the Circus to see what all the noise
was about. It was something tremendously
important to dogs in general, no doubt. But
the little red dog, the little liar, had no sooner
been overtaken and passed by the other, than
back he ran, and picking up the bone, made off
with it in the opposite direction. Very soon the
lurcher returned and appeared astonished and
puzzled at the disappearance of his bone. There
I left him, still looking for it and sniffing at
the open shop doors. He perhaps thought in
his simplicity that some kind lady had picked
it up and left it with one of the shopmen to
be claimed by its rightful owner.

      I had heard of such actions on the
part of dogs before, but always with a smile;
for we know the people who tell this kind of

story - the dog-worshippers, or canophilists as
they are sometimes called, a people weak in
their intellectuals, and as a rule unveracious,
although probably not consciously so. But now
I had myself witnessed this thing, which, when
read, will perhaps cause others to smile in
their turn.

But what is one to say of such an
action? Just now we are all of us, philosophers
included, in a muddle over the questions of mind
and intellect in the lower animals, and just how
much of each element goes to the composition
of any one act; but probably most persons
would say at once that the action of the little
red dog in Regent Street was purely intelligent.
I am not sure. The swiftness, smoothness, and
certainty with which the whole thing was
carried out gave it the appearance of a
series of automatic movements rather than a
reasoned act which had never been rehearsed.

Recently during my country rambles
I have been on the look-out for the small red

dog, and have met with several interesting
examples in the southern counties. One, in
Hampshire, moved me to laughter like that
small animal at Charterhouse Hinton.

  This was at Sway, a village near
Lymington. A boy, mounted on a creaking old
bike, was driving some cows to the common,
and had the greatest difficulty in keeping on
while following behind the lazy beasts on a
rough track among the furze bushes; and behind the boy at a distance of ten yards trotted
the little red dog, tongue out, looking as happy
and proud as possible. As I passed him he
looked back at me as if to make sure that I
had seen him and noted that he formed part of
that important procession. On another day I
went to the village and renewed my acquaintance with the little fellow and heard his history.
Everybody praised him for his affectionate
disposition and his value as a watch-dog by
night, and I was told that his mother, now
dead, had been greatly prized, and was the

smallest red dog ever seen in that part of
Hampshire.

Some day one of the thousand writers
on "man's friend" will conceive the happy idea
of a chapter or two on the dog - the universal
cur - and he will then perhaps find it necessary
to go abroad to study this well - marked dwarf
variety, for with us he has fallen on evil
days. There is no doubt that the muzzling
order profoundly affected the character of our
dog population, since it went far towards the
destruction of the cur and of mongrels - the
races already imperilled by the extraordinary
predominance of the fox-terrier. The change
was most marked in the metropolis, and after
Mr. Long's campaign I came to the conclusion
that here at all events the little red dog had
been exirpated . He, with other varieties of
the cur, was the dog of the poor, and when
the muzzle deprived him of the power to fend
for himself, he became a burden to his
master. But I was mistaken ; he is still

152

with us, even here in london, though now very rare.

W.H. Hudson   1841-1922
The little Red Dog.

THE CHAPS GAVE I A PUPPY: the value which a navvy placed on his hound.

'There ain't no such chaps for poaching as they navigators in all England: I means where there be a railway a-making. I've knowed forty of 'em go out together on a Sunday, and every man had a dog, and some two; and good dogs too - lots of 'em as you wouldn't buy for ten quid. They used to spread out like, and sweep the fields clean as the crown of your hat. Keepers weren't no good at all, and besides they never knowed which place us was going to make for. One of the chaps gave I a puppy, and he growed into the finest greyhound as you'd find in a day's walk. The first time I was took up before the bench I had to go to goal, because the contractor had broke and the works was stopped, so that my mates hadn't no money to pay the fine.

The dog was took away home to

granny by my butty (comrade), but one of
the gentlemen as seed it in the court sent
his groom over and got it off the old woman
for five pound. She thought if I hadn't the hound
I should give it up, and she come and paid me
out of goal. It was a wonder as I didn't break
her neck ; only her was a good woman, you
see, to I. But I wouldn't have parted with
that hound for a quart-full of sovereigns.
Many's a time I've seed his name - They
changed his name, of course - in the papers
for winning coursing matches. But we let
that gent as bought him have it warm :
we harried his pheasants and killed the most
of 'em.

Richard Jeffries,   1848 ~ 1887.
The Amateur Poacher.

DOGS REVERTED TO THREE SORTS IN THE WILD.

The dogs, of course, like the cats, were forced by starvation into the fields, where they perished in incredible numbers. Of many species of dogs which are stated to have been plentiful among the ancients, we have now nothing but the name. The poodle is extinct, the Maltese terrier, the Pomeranian, the Italian greyhound, and, it is believed, great numbers of crosses and mongrels have utterly disappeared. There was none to feed them, and they could not find food for themselves, nor could they stand the rigour of the winter when exposed to the frost in the open air. Some kinds, more hardy and fitted by nature for the chase, became wild, and their descendants are now found in the woods. Of these, there are three sorts which keep apart from each other, and are thought not to interbreed. The most numerous are the black. The black wood-dog is short and stoutly made, with shaggy hair, sometimes marked with white patches.

There can be no doubt that it is the
descendant of the ancient sheep-dog, for it is
known that the sheep-dog was of that
character, and it is said that those who used
to keep sheep soon found their dogs abandon
the fold, and join the wild troops that fell
upon the sheep. The black wood-dogs hunt in
packs of ten or more (as many as forty have
been counted), and are the pest of the farmer,
for, unless his flocks are protected at night
within stockades or enclosures, they are
certain to be attacked. Not satisfied with
killing enough to satisfy hunger, these dogs
tear and mangle for sheer delight of blood,
and will destroy twenty times as many as
they can eat, leaving the miserably torn
carcases on the field. Nor are the sheep
always safe by day if the wood-dogs happen
to be hungry. The shepherd is, therefore,
usually accompanied by two or three mastiffs,
of whose great size and strength the others

stand in awe. At night, and when in large
packs, starving in the snow, not even mastiffs
can check them.

No wood-dog, of any kind, has ever
been known to attack man, and the hunter
in the forest hears their bark in every
direction without fear. It is, nevertheless,
best to retire out of their way when charging
sheep in packs, for they then seem seized
with a blind fury, and some who have
endeavoured to fight them have been thrown
down and seriously mauled. But this has
been in the blindness of their rush; no instance has ever been known of their purposely
attacking man.

These black wood-dogs will also
chase and finally pull down cattle, if they
can get within the enclosures, and even
horses have fallen victims to their untiring
thirst for blood. Not even the wild cattle can
always escape, despite their strength, and they
have been known to run down stags, though

not their usual quarry.

The next kind of wild wood-dog is the yellow, a smaller animal, with smooth hair inclining to a yellow colour, which lives principally upon game, chasing all from the hare to the stag. It is as swift, or nearly as swift, as the greyhound, and possesses greater endurance. In coursing the hare, it not uncommonly happens that these dogs start from the brake and take the hare, when nearly exhausted, from the hunter's hounds. They will in the same way follow a stag, which has been almost run down by the hunter's, and bring him to bay, though in this case they lose their booty, dispersing through fear of man, when the hunters come up in a body.

But such is their love of the chase, that they are known to assemble from their lairs at the distant sound of the horn, and, as the hunters ride through the woods, they often see the yellow dogs flitting along side by side with them through bush and fern.

These animals sometimes hunt singly, sometimes in couples, and as the season advances,
and winter approaches, in packs of eight or
twelve. They never attack sheep or cattle,
and avoid man, except when they perceive he
is engaged in the chase. There is little doubt
that they are the descendants of the dogs
which the ancients called lurchers, crossed,
perhaps, with the greyhound, and possibly other
breeds. When the various species of dogs were
thrown on their own resources, those only
withstood the exposure and hardships which
were naturally hardy, and possessed natural
aptitude for the chase.

The third species of wood-dog is the
white. They are low on the legs, of a dingy
white colour, and much smaller than the
other two. They neither attack cattle nor game
though fond of hunting rabbits. This dog is, in
fact, a scavenger, living upon the carcases
of dead sheep and animals, which are found
picked clean in the night. For this purpose

it haunts the neighbourhood of habitations,
and prowls in the evening over heaps of refuse,
scampering away at the least alarm, for it
is extremely timid.

It is perfectly harmless, for even
the poultry do not dread it, and it will not
face a tame cat, if by chance the two meet.
It is rarely met with far from habitations,
though it will accompany an army on the
march. It may be said to remain in one district. The black and yellow dogs, on the contrary
roam about the forest without apparent
home. One day the hunter sees signs of their
presence, and perhaps may, for a month
afterwards, not so much as hear a bark.

This uncertainty in the case of the
black dog is the bane of the shepherds; for,
not seeing or hearing anything of the enemy
for months altogether, in spite of former
experience their vigilance relaxes, and
suddenly, while they sleep, their flocks are
scattered. We still have, among tame dogs,

the mastiff, terrier, spaniel, deerhound, and greyhound, all of which are as faithful to man as ever.

Richard Jefferies   1848~1887.
After London.

DOGS EVERYWHERE.

There are dogs under the tables and
chairs; dogs in the window-seat; dogs panting
on the stone flags of the passage, after a sharp
trot behind a trap, choosing the coolest spot to loll
their red tongues out; dogs outside in the road;
dogs standing on hind legs, and painfully lapping
the water in the horse-trough; and there is a
yelping of puppies in the distance. The cushions
of the sofa are strewn with dogs' hairs, and once
now and then a dog leisurely hops up the stair-
case.   Customers are served by the landlady,
a decent body enough in her way: her son, the man
of the house, is up in the 'orchard' at the rear,
feeding his dogs. Where the 'orchard' ends in a
paddock stands a small shed: in places the
thatch on the roof has fallen through in the
course of years and revealed bare rafters.
The bottom part of the door has decayed, and
the long nose of a greyhound is thrust out
sniffing through a hole. Dickon, the said son,
is delighted to undo the padlock for a visitor

who is 'squire'. In an instant the long hounds
leap up, half a dozen at a time, and I
stagger backwards, forced by the sheer
vigour of their caresses against the door-
post. Dickon cannot quell the uproarious
pack: he kicks the door open, and away
they scamper round and round the paddock at
headlong speed.

What a joy it is to them to stretch
their limbs! I forget the squalor of the
kennel in watching their happy gambols. I
cannot drink more than one tumbler of
brown brandy and water; but Dickon overlooks
that weakness, feeling that I admire his grey
-hounds. It is arranged that I am to see them
work in the autumn.

The months pass, and in his trap with
the famous trotter in the shafts we roll up
the village street. Applebloom and golden fruit
too are gone, and the houses show more now
among the bare trees; but as the rim of the
ruddy November sun comes forth from the edge

of a cloud there appears a buff tint everywhere
in the background. When elm and ash are
bare the oaks retain their leaves, and these
are illumined by the autumn beams. Over-
topped by tall elms and hidden by the orchards,
the oaks were hardly seen in summer; now
they are found to be numerous and give the
prevailing line to the place.

Dickon taps the dashboard as the
mare at last tops the hill, and away she
speeds along the level plateau for the downs.
Two greyhounds are with us; two more have
gone on under the charge of a boy. Skirting the
hills a mile or two, we presently leave the
road and drive over the turf: there is no track,
but Dickon knows his way. The rendezvous is
a small fir plantation, the young trees in
which are but shoulder-high. Below is a plain
entirely surrounded by the hills, and partly
green with root crops: more than one flock of
sheep is down there, and two teams ploughing
the stubble. Neither the ploughmen nor the

shepherds take the least heed of us, except to watch for the sport. The spare couple are fastened in the trap; the boy jumps up and takes the reins. Dickon puts the slip on the couple that are to run first, and we begin to range.

Just at the foot of the hill the grass is tall and grey; there, too, are the dead dry stalks of many plants that cultivation has driven from the ploughed fields and that find a refuge at the edge. A hare starts from the very verge and makes up the downs. Dickon slips the hounds, and a faint halloo comes from the shepherds and the ploughmen. It is a beautiful sight to see hounds bound over the sward; the sinewy back bends like a bow, but a bow that, instead of an arrow, shoots itself; the deep chests drink the air. Is there any moment so joyful in life as the second when the chase begins? As we gaze, before we even step forward, the hare is over the ridge and out of sight. Then we race and tear up the slope; then the boy in the trap flaps the reins and away goes the mare out of sight too.

Dickon is long and rawboned, a powerful fellow, strong of limb, and twice my build; but he sips too often at the brown brandy, and after the first burst I can head him. But he knows the hills and the route the hare will take, so that I have but to keep pace In five minutes as we cross a ridge we see the game again; the hare is circling back - she passes under us not fifty yards away, as we stand panting on the hill. The youngest hound gains and runs right over her; she doubles, the older hound picks up the running. By a furze-bush she doubles again; but the young one turns her - the next moment she is in the jaws of the old dog.

Again and again the hounds are slipped, now one couple, now the other: we pant, and we can scarcely speak with running, but the wild excitement of the horn and the sweet pure air of the downs supply fresh strength. The little lad brings the mare anywhere : through the furze, among the flint - pits, jolting over the ruts, she rattles along with sure alacrity. There are five hares in the sack under the straw when at last we get up and slowly drive down to the highway, reaching it some two miles from where we left it . Dickon sends the dogs home by the boy on foot ; we drive round and return to the village by a different route, entering it from the opposite direction.

Richard Jefferies,   1848 ~ 1887.
The Amateur Poacher.

THE SPORTSMAN'S DISTRESS.

I've lost my friend, my dog, and wife,
        Saved only horse and purse;
Yet when I think on human life,
        Thank heaven it is no worse.

My friend was sickly, poor, and old,
        Was peevish, blind, and crippled;
My wife was ugly and a scold, —
        I rather think she tippled.

My dog was faithful, fond, and true,
        In sporting gave me pleasure;
I shouldn't care for t'other two,
        If I had saved this treasure.

Anon,

HORACE IN HAND, BUT BECKFORD IN HIS HEAD :
Parson Jack Russell's encounter with Trump.

It was on a glorious afternoon
towards the end of May, when strolling round
Magdalen meadow with Horace in hand, but
Beckford in his head, he emerged from the
classic shade of Addison's Walk, crossed the
Cherwell in a punt, and passed over in the
direction of Marston, hoping to devote an hour
or two to study in the quiet meads of that
hamlet, near the charming slopes of Elsfield,
or in the deeper and more secluded haunts of
Shotover Wood. But before he had reached
Marston a milkman met him with a terrier—
such an animal as Russell had as yet only
seen in his dreams; he halted, as Actaeon
might have done when he caught sight of
Diana disporting in her bath ; but ; unlike
that ill-fated hunter, he never budged from
the spot till he had won the prize and secured
it for his own. She was called Trump, and became
the progenitress of that famous race of

terriers which, from that day to the present,
have been associated with Russell's name
at home and abroad - his able and keen
coadjutors in the hunting - field. An oil -
painting of Trump is still in existance, and is,
I believe, possessed by H.R.H. the Prince of
Wales; but as a copy, executed by a fair and
talented artist, is now in my possession,
and was acknowledged by Russell to be not
only an admirable likeness of the original,
but equally good as a type of the race in
general, I will try, however imperfectly, to
describe the portrait as it now lies before me.

In the first place, the colour is white
with just a patch of dark tan over each eye
and ear, while a similar dot, not larger than
a penny piece, marks the root of the tail. The
coat, which is, thick, close, and a trifle wiry,
is well calculated to protect the body from wet
and cold, but has no affinity with the long,
rough jacket of a Scotch terrier. The legs are
straight as arrows, the feet perfect; the

loins and conformation of the whole frame
indicative of hardihood and endurance;
while the size and height of the animal may be
compared to that of a full-grown vixen fox.

"I seldom or ever see a real fox-
terrier nowadays," said Russell recently to a
friend who was inspecting a dog show contain-
ing a hundred and fifty entries under that
denomination; "they have so intermingled
strange blood with the real article, that, if
he were not informed, it would puzzle Professor
Bell himself to discover what race the so-
called fox-terrier belongs to."

E.W.L. Davies
Memoir of the Rev. John Russell and
his out-of-door life
pub. 1902.

THE INFLUENCE OF CANINE EXHIBITIONS.

It is not necessary, in a work of this kind, to discuss the vexed question of the influence of canine exhibitions on the sporting dog. Much good has been done by these; but, alas! also much evil. The sporting dog, however, has suffered less than most other breeds, and on the whole, in the writer's opinion, distinct benefit has accrued, except in the case of the spaniel breed. This is due to the fact that dogs of other breeds have not been tampered with to the same extent as the spaniel has by "fanciers," whose handiwork is seen in the numerous grotesque creatures which appear on the bench, and, with considerable difficulty, are able to walk a few times round the judge's ring. With these, however, the gamekeeper has nothing to do. The breed is right enough, but by selection a non-sporting class has produced an animal unfitted for work owing to the exhibitors' want

of knowledge and the apathy of other classes.
One must remember, however, that those are
selected specimens, and that it is possible to
find animals of the same breed which are fit
and able for fieldwork.

E.W.L. Davies
Memoir of the Rev. John Russell.

PARSON JOHN RUSSELL : an obituary

Though fiction in a past generation
gave us a Parson Adams, there is no likelihood
of a nearer prototype of that worthy than the
kind old clergyman who passed quietly away
just ten days ago. The resemblance between
the country parson of the novelist and the Rev.
John Russell ends, however, at the point where
both are seen to exercise an influence upon
all those with whom they came in contact,
and in an honesty of purpose to be constantly
helping others out of scrapes or troubles. This
was the character of John Russell; but he was
a greater gentleman than Parson Adams, and
his journey through life may be looked upon as
an odd sort of mixture between the old-fashioned
parson, the country gentleman, and the courtier.
In his parish he was the adviser and the friend
of his flock, at cover-side or at the agricultural
meeting he was hearty and well met with
everyone, and in the hall of the palace he
was polished and affable to a degree. It is no
wonder, therefore, that he was a universal

favourite, from the prince to the peasant, and it is possible that no one has ever surpassed him as an arbitrator and peace-maker in every sort of circle. He would travel third-class from Devonshire to Yorkshire for no other purpose, and whether in bringing together broken ties, or preaching a chantry sermon, he had a way of his own of reaching the heart that few could equal and no one could surpass.

Born a sportsman, he never thought it incompatible with duty to join in every sort of legitimate sport and pastime; and besides being the most genuine fox hunter in the country, it was by no means unusual to see his well known figure at Ascot or Stockbridge, or on the box of a friend's drag in the coaching-season. There was no cant or humbug about John Russell; he performed the duties of his religious profession better than the majority of clergymen, and he was ever ready to join in anything to promote sport or fellowship among sportsmen.

great that, as soon as hounds were out of
cover some of his terriers have gone ten miles,
and reached well-known earths in time to
stop a fox from entering a destination that
he had been making for. This Mr Russell
thought was the highest character that
could be found in a terrier, and he would
have none that hesitated to go to ground,
but he liked them to tease or worry a fox
rather than to kill him or fight him.
He said his terriers worked for the pack, and
knew as well as he did what they were wanted
for. The Jack Russell terrier was hardly as
big as a modern show terrier; in working
condition the dogs would be no more than 15lb.
and many of them barely that, and five-
and-twenty years ago they formed a very
distinct type. Since that time they have
been crossed on to other strains, and their
uniformity has been probably lost, though
they live in all the descendants of 'Foiler'.
Mr Russell started his breed at Oxford when

The writer of these lines asked him, when the Kennel Club was established to join as a member, and he was quite delighted with the idea, and has been a member ever since. It will be remembered that Mr Russell judged the fox-terriers at the Crystal Palace for the Club in 1875, and although the old gentleman was not altogether at home with all the requirements of the modern fox-terriers, he was greatly pleased with all he saw at the show, and expressed to us the very strong admiration he had for 'Rattler'.

Mr Russell's own breed of fox-terriers were wire-haired, and his greatest aversion were those that had in them any signs of a bull-cross. A real fox-terrier, he would say, is not meant to murder, and his intelligence should always keep him from such a crime. Thus he boasted that the best he ever had never tasted blood to his knowledge, but that they could not lose their way, and that their eye to country and memory were so he was eighteen, so something like seventy years ago, and he has his pedigrees that he could trace to from the time he started them.

As the oldest fox-terrier breeder in England Mr Russell's connection with the Kennel Club was an honour to that body, and we personally regret the loss of a very old friend in the fine old English gentleman who has been recently gathered to his fathers; and that a thousand followed him to his grave that were nearly all of them sportsmen shows that our slight contribution, as well as many others written by staunch friends and admirers, is largely shared in sentiment to the memory of the Rev. John Russell

From the "Kennel Gazette"
May 1883.

ON CATS AND DOGS.

What I've suffered from them this morning no tongue can tell. It began with Gustavus Adolphus. Gustavus Adolphus (they call him "Gusty" downstairs for short) is a very good sort of dog, when he is in the middle of a large field, or on a fairly extensive common, but I won't have him in-doors. He means well, but this house is not his size. He stretches himself, and over go two chairs and a what-not. He wags his tail, and the room looks as if a devastating army had marched through it. He breathes, and it puts the fire out.

At dinner-time, he creeps in under the table, lies there for a while, and then gets up suddenly; the first intimation we have of his movements being given by the table, which appears animated by a desire to turn somersaults. We all clutch at it frantically, and endeavour to maintain it in a horiz-ontal position; whereupon his struggles, he being under the impression that some wicked conspiracy is being hatched against him, become fearful, and the final picture presented is generally that of an overturned table and a smashed-up dinner, sandwiched between two sprawling layers of infuriated men and women.

He came in this morning in his usual style, which he appears to have founded on that of an American cyclone, and the first thing he did was to sweep my coffee cup off the table with his tail, sending the contents full into the middle of my waistcoat.

I rose from my chair, hurriedly, and remarking, "―――――", approached him at a rapid rate. He preceded me in the direction of the door. At the door, he met Eliza, coming in with eggs. Eliza observed, "Ugh!" and sat down on the floor, the eggs took up different positions about the carpet, where they spread themselves out, and Gustavus Adolphus left the room. I called after him, strongly advising him to go straight downstairs, and not let me see him again for the next hour or so; and he, seeming to agree with me, dodged the coal-scoop, and went; while I returned, dried myself, and finished breakfast. I made sure that he had gone into the yard, but when I looked into the passage ten minutes later, he was sitting at the top of the stairs. I ordered him down at once, but he only barked and jumped about, so I went to see what was the matter.

Jerome. K. Jerome.   1859 ~ 1927.

AN ANGEL SENT UPON THE EARTH, for some reason in the shape of a small fox-terrier.

We therefore decided that we would sleep out on fine nights, and hotel it, and inn it, and pub it, like respectable folks, when it was wet, or when we felt inclined for a change.

Montmorency hailed this compromise with much approval. He does not revel in romantic solitude. Give him something noisy; and if a trifle low, so much the jollier. To look at Montmorency you would imagine that he was an angel sent upon the earth, for some reason with held from mankind, in the shape of a small fox-terrier. There is a sort of Oh-what-a-wicked-world-this-is-and-how-I-wish-I-could-do-something-to-make-it-better-and-nobler expression about Montmorency that has been known to bring tears into the eyes of pious old ladies and gentlemen.

When first he came to live at my expense, I never thought I should be able to get

him to stop long. I used to sit down and look at
him, as he sat on the rug and looked up at me,
and think : " Oh, that dog will never live. He
will be snatched up to the bright skies in a
chariot, that is what will happen to him ".

But, when I had paid for about a
dozen chickens that he had killed ; and had
dragged him, growling and kicking, by the scruff
of his neck, out of a hundred and fourteen street
fights ; and had had a dead cat brought round for
my inspection by an irate female, who called me
a murderer ; and had been summoned by the
man next door but one for having a ferocious
dog at large, that had kept him pinned up in
his own tool-shed, afraid to venture his nose
outside the door for over two hours on a cold
night ; and had learned that the gardener,
unknown to myself, had won thirty shillings
by backing him to kill rats against time,
then I began to think that maybe they'd
let him remain on earth for a bit longer,
after all.

To hang about a stable, and collect
a gang of the most disreputable dogs to be found
in the room, and lead them out to march
round the slums to fight other disreputable dogs,
is Montmorency's idea of "life"; and so, as I
before observed, he gave to the suggestion of
inns, and pubs, and hotels his most emphatic
approbation.

Jerome K. Jerome.
Three Men in a Boat.

DOGS CAN'T DYE THEIR OWN HAIR, LIKE LADIES DO.
Schweik is alive and well.

'Do you know how to treat animals? Are you really fond of them?'

'Well, sir' said Schweik, 'I like dogs best, because it's a paying game if you know how to sell them. It's not in my line, because I'm too honest, but people used to come bothering me, all the same, because they said I sold them a pup, as you might say, sir, instead of a sound, thorough-bred dog. As if all dogs can be sound and thorough-bred. And then they always wanted a pedigree, so I had to have pedigrees printed and turn a mongrel, that was born in a brick works, into a pure-bred pedigree dog. Oh, you'd be surprised, sir, at the way all the big dog fanciers swindle their customers over pedigrees. Of course, there ain't many dogs that could truthfully call themselves out-and-out thoroughbreds. Sometimes the mother or the grandmother got mixed up with some mongrel or other, or maybe several, and then the animal takes after each of them. Ears from one, tail from another, whiskers from another, jowls from a fourth, bandy legs from a fifth, size from a sixth; and if a dog had a dozen connections of that sort, you can just imagine, sir, what he looks like. I once bought a dog like that, Balaban his name was, and he had so many parents he was that ugly that all the other dogs kept out of his way, and I only bought him because I was sorry for the animal being deserted, like. And he used to squat at home all day long in a corner, and he was always so down in the mouth that I had to sell him as a fox terrier. What gave me the most trouble was dyeing him to make him piebald. The man who bought him took him away to Moravia, and I haven't laid eyes on him since.'

The lieutenant began to take a great interest in this doggy lore, and so Schweik was able to continue without hindrance:

'Dogs can't dye their own hair, like ladies do, so that's always a job for the one who wants to sell him. When a dog's so old that he's all grey, and you want to sell him as a one-year pup, you buy some silver nitrate,

pound it up and then paint the dog black so that
he looks like new. And to give him more strength
you feed him arsenic like they do horses, and you
clean his teeth with emery paper like they
use to clean rusty knives with. And before you
show him to a customer, you make him swallow
brandy, so that he gets a bit tipsy and then he's
merry and bright and barks as jolly as can be,
and chums up with everyone, like people do when
they've boozed. But this is the most important
part of the business, sir. You must talk to the
customers, keep on talking to 'em, till they've
sort of flabbergasted. If a man wants to buy
a house dog and all you've got is a greyhound,
you've got to have the gift of the gab, as they
say, to talk the man over, so that he takes the
greyhound instead of a house dog. Or supposing
someone wants a savage bulldog to keep burg-
lars away, you've got to bamboozle him so that
instead of a bulldog he takes one of these here
midget lapdogs away in his pocket. When I
used to deal in animals, there was a lady came

one day and said that her parrot had flown away
into the front garden and that some boys who
were playing at Indians in front of her house
had caught this parrot and torn all the feathers
out of its tail and decorated themselves with them
like policemen . Well, this parrot felt so ashamed
at losing his tail that he fell ill and a vet had
finished him off with some powders . So she wanted
to buy a new parrot , a well - behaved one, not
one of those vulgar birds that can do nothing but
swear . Well, what was I to do, not having any
parrot and not knowing where to lay hands on
one ? But I had a bad-tempered bulldog , quite
blind he was too. And I give you my word, sir,
I had to talk to that lady from four in the afternoon till seven in the evening, before she bought
the blind bulldog instead of the parrot. That was
a more ticklish job than any of their diplomatic
stuff, and when she was going away, I said to her:
"Those little boys had better not try to pull his
tail off." And that's the last words I spoke to
that lady, because she had to move away from

Prague on account of that bulldog, because he bit everyone in the house. You wouldn't believe, sir, how hard it is to get hold of a really first-rate animal.'

'I'm very fond of dogs,' said the lieutenant. 'Some of my pals who've at the front have got dogs with them, and they write and tell me that the company of a faithful and devoted animal makes life in the trenches quite pleasant. Well, you seem to have a thorough knowledge of dogs, and I hope that if I have one you'll look after him properly. What breed do you consider the best? I mean, for a dog as a companion. I once had a fox terrier, but I don't know–'

'Oh, I think a fox terrier is a very nice dog, sir. Of course, it's not everyone who takes to them, because they've got bristles and tough whiskers that makes them look like discharged convicts. They're so ugly that it makes them look quite handsome, and they're clever animals, too. St Bernards ain't in it with them. Oh, yes, they're clever and no mistake.

I once knew one ——'

Lieutenant Lukash looked at his
watch and interrupted Schweik's flow of talk.

'Well, it's getting late and I must be
off to bed. To-morrow I'm on duty again, so you'
ve got the whole day to find your fox terrier.'

Jaroslav Hasek,
The Good Soldier Schweik.

GALLANT LAAL WORKERS : a hunting song
praising the terrier

Now there's mony a song about hunting,
Packs and huntsmen are honoured by name,
But there isn't a song about terriers
Which in Lakeland howe gained lasting fame.

Chorus.
So always remember your terriers,
Protect them from wet and from cold,
For the love of a tyke for his master
Can never be measured in gold.

Whether its Fury or Trixie or Nellie,
Or Rock, Jock or Turk it's the same,
One quality you'll find among them,
And dalesfolk call it "dead game".
And whether he's rough or smooth-coated,
He'll tackle badger, otter or fox,
Run adrain or creep into a soil-hole,
Or squeeze through a girke in the rocks.

He'll yield not one inch though they maul him,
He'll fight to the death on his own,

Though sometimes he'll be imprisoned
By a rush-in of soil or of stone.
And then the brave lads of the valleys
To save him will toil day and night,
And join in a Hallo of triumph
As he blinks back to God's blessed light.

Now at Cruft's famous show down in London,
They have Lakelands that aren't worth the name
If you showed 'em a fox or an otter
They'd fly for their lives without shame.
They're not built to creep or do battle,
But to sit on a chair in a house,
And they do say that one recent champion
Was chased down the road by a mouse!

So here's to our gallant laal workers,
Not beauties, perhaps, but they'll do.
With gameness they've also affection,

And make you a pal good and true.
And when your terrier, in old age, is dying,
And the world all about you seems sad,
A lick on the hand will console you,
For a truer friend man never had.

D. P. Todd
The Terrier Song
Tune "Laal Mellbreak".

EVERY PACK OF ANY STANDING MAINTAINS A FEW HOUNDS:

Modern hunting people are rather prejud-
iced against the hounds because they are so apt to
get under horses' feet when they are jumping fences,
or in full gallop over wheat. But tradition is tradition, and every pack of any standing maintains
a few hounds for Peterborough, and the Puppy Show, and
to go about with the huntsman when he passes
the village inns. Always remember hounds are counted
in couples. It is important to mention this, as sometimes you hear it said the huntsman must have
had a couple. That refers to his duties.

In the good old days before huntsmen knew
so much and rode so fast the hounds were expected to
find their fox and hunt him too. As no one knew
the exact spot where a fox might be it was
customary, while the hounds were busied about
their duties, for the hunt staff and the members
of the Field to combat the inclement weather
within a tavern. Now it is quite obvious when
the hounds pushed up their fox that unless they
let the huntsman know there would be disappointment all round. So it was absolutely

essential that every hound possessed a resonant, carrying, long distance call. A secondary, but by no means unworthy ambition of every Master, was that the music of a pack should harmonise. There might be small hounds with penetrating sopranos, or huge hounds with reverberating basses, or medium hounds with throaty tenors. But harmonise they must. So in old records you may still see, if you can find any (which we must admit we have failed to do), a Master thanking Providence that he can trace back his eminent mezzo-contralto Plaintive to that great basso-profundo Qvorn Caroller.

Only in Wales to-day does this reverence for hound music survive. Why is that? This is the first time the truth has been revealed. It is entirely due to the national weakness for local eisteddfods, which are competitions in voice endurance either alone or in parties of resolute friends. In many a lonely cottage, all through the winter months, grandfather and grandmother, parents, Auntie

Rebecca from Bwlch-y-gwlch and the man who feeds the calves - all of them inflamed with high tea and indigestion - sing without cessation for eight hours, by the old kitchen clock, that passionate summons "Awake Beloved" to the tune of Aberystwyth. Consequently hound puppies who have been walked in such melodious homes acquire a range of tongue which is never heard with the Bicester. Indeed, its practical object has in these modern times quite disappeared. For one thing, everyone (even the huntsman) knows just where a fox will be found and in which direction he is bound to run. In fact, only very athletic and carefully dieted foxes can hope to keep much ahead of members who are trying out blood horses with an idea of Cheltenham or Aintree. For another thing, as the influence of the city must be scrupulously observed in these hard times, a mute hound does not make such an infernal rumpus when a large subscriber lands on his stern over a post and rails.

Now about the puppies. A whelp is the innocent with the trustful gaze who is walked by those simple persons who hope they will win the silver cup for the parlour window. A puppy does not become a hound until he has eaten all the hens and killed all the cats at the farm where he is walked, taken his place in the Puppy Show, and met the huntsman.

Every Hunt must have a Puppy Show because that is how a Master has his young entry kept and fed and taught incurable habits for nothing. Puppies enter to fox in the cubbing season. As they have hitherto entered to everything else it is quite a new thrill for them. The Puppy Show is held in order that the simpletons who have walked a puppy, or even a couple, may put on their Sunday clothes and realise how much better their puppy looks than the other people's.

Puppies are destructive, expensive, homicidal and full of sorrow. Fortunately they never live. It is rumoured that some busybody has invented a vaccine which will preserve them from distemper. That is, we suppose, what short-sighted people call Progress. Do we speak too strongly? Without a surplus of puppies there will be no puppy walkers, and without puppy walkers no Puppy Show. Don't forget that a fifty to one chance for a prize, a dish of tea and the Master's speech, is about all the farmer's wife gets out of the Hunt. And if the farmer's wife loses interest, what then? What indeed! Where's your precious vaccine now?

It is customary at a Puppy Show for the Master to invite two or even three fellow Masters to come over and judge his puppies. With a devisive smile these Masters accept. They arrive and put on kennel coats, and have little books, and look very knowing indeed. In a ring, where all the walkers can see their puppies dragged and propelled about, the judging goes on for hours and hours. The only other functions comparable to it in length of time, solemnity, and absence of all spiritual or physical

compensations is the pibroch playing at a Highland gathering.

After the judging is over, the whole
party, with hosts of members, strangers, farmers,
and all their friends troop towards the tea-tent.
Here the Master - whose smile has never
fluctuated throughout the day - is surrounded
by his fellow - Masters of all kinds - even of
beagles and otter hounds, so broken down are
social distinctions on that great day.

After tea - with which cold beef and
ham may be eaten if the Master can run to
it - the prizes are presented. Then come the
speeches. These are always given by the same
people at every Hunt because it is absolutely
essential that the right thing is said every
year. After the most coherent visiting Master
has congratulated the Hunt on such an
unusually fine show of puppies, old Mr. Dumble-
day gets up to speak for the farmers. There is
one of his sort in every Hunt. He has retired
long enough to forget what farming is really like

or possibly he has lived so long he goes back before
the bad times, or he mayn't have been a farmer
at all. But apart from that he has spent an
hour with the Hunt Secretary, who writes all
the speeches anyhow, for fear they don't stop.
Mr. Cracklethorpe, the Field Master's gamekeeper (who either has a fox in the home
coverts or concocts his own advertisement
for The Field), then deprecates the notions of
some keepers who blame the fox for their own
lack of knowledge. He recalls instances of
vixens adopting pheasant poults who had lost
their mother (he doesn't say how). There is
then a steady old subscriber to express the
feelings of the gathering towards the Master.
Finally the Master rises, and nervously
consulting his notes from time to time, makes
the Masters's famous speech.

What now about the hounds?

Well, there are hounds and Welsh
hounds. The English hound is a depressed-looking
replica of another English hound. The Welsh

hound looks like no other hound, nor like a
hound at all. It prefers to wear its hair on end,
is voracious, and usually lurks in a butcher's
shop. But it can kill foxes. In fact, it can
kill anything. On hunting days in Wales
Secretaries advise farmers to shut up all
stock smaller than a Hereford cow. Welsh
hounds, through what advanced French
scholars call "joie de vivre", will hunt any
line from the postman reading the morning
mail to the widow's only nanny-goat, and
they will speak with authority and all together to anything from a weasel to the
Vicar's Angora rabbits. The Welsh hound is also
useful for sheepdog trials in the summer, because
it keeps him in practice for riot later on, and
may earn a bit in between.

There are harriers and beagles, but
no real gentleman knows much about these.
The harrier chases a hare in small circles,
so that members can pull one rein and still
maintain the usual grip on the saddle. When

the hare crosses the same field for the seventh
time, how the farmer cheers and waves his
hat. The beagle is smaller and therefore eats
less. It is followed quite a long way off by
persons of maturity acting under medical advice.

To establish a pack is child's play.
The proper procedure is to write a nice boyish
letter to some Master - anyone will do - and put
yourself in his hands. Explain that you have
money but no practical knowledge (because he
will reply more quickly then), and that you feel
it is cheaper in the end to pay a generous
figure for really good hounds, which will hunt all
day and kill foxes all the time and be steady,
and not eat the sandwiches at the Meets. Don't
lose your head if he puts through a long-distance
call.

The Master will invite you down to his
kennels either for the night or for luncheon. (No-
one ever sees kennels before a hearty meal.)
When he has explained that he has the best
pack and huntsman in England you will know

your luck is in. But be prepared for a rather
trying scene. It happens when the Master tells
the huntsman he has decided to part with old
Chorister. The huntsman will start back and in
a strangled voice exclaim: " Not old Chorister,
Sir !" proving, beyond cavil, what a one old
Chorister must be. Himself considerably moved,
the Master will explain. He will say that you
are a beginner going to hunt hounds yourself
and that Masters must cling together.

      You will be surprised when you see
old Chorister. He will strike your inexperienced
eye as very old, very tired, and extremely deaf.
But you will know by his price you must be
mistaken. Dreadnought, Captain, Hornet, and
Champion will also be yours. As they are all
sixth season hounds they have nothing to learn,
and will in fact teach you far more than you
might suspect.

      If you pay half a dozen calls like
that you will have your pack, and very soon will
know where you are. You will also know where

they are. Some will have kennel lameness. The rest will follow you about in covert with dog-like devotion or tarry with the Field. Never mind. Console yourself with the thought that some day you will get a letter too.

Frederick Watson
Hunting Pie.